Everyday Mathematics®

Student Math Journal 2

The University of Chicago
School Mathematics Project

A Division of The McGraw·Hill Companies

Columbus, Ohio
Chicago, Illinois

UCSMP Elementary Materials Component

Max Bell, Director

Authors

Max Bell
Jean Bell
John Bretzlauf*
Amy Dillard*
Robert Hartfield
Andy Isaacs*
James McBride, Director
Kathleen Pitvorec*
Peter Saecker

Technical Art

Diana Barrie*

*Second Edition only

Photo Credits

Phil Martin/Photography, Jack Demuth/Photography, Cover Credits: Sand, starfish, orange wedges, crystal/Bill Burlingham Photography, Photo Collage: Herman Adler Design Group

www.sra4kids.com

SRA/McGraw-Hill
A Division of The McGraw-Hill Companies

Send all inquiries to:
SRA/McGraw-Hill
P.O. BOX 812960
Chicago, IL 60681

Printed in the United States of America.

ISBN 1-57039-840-2

10 11 12 DBH 07 06 05 04

Contents

Unit 7: Multiplication and Division

A note at the bottom of each journal page indicates when that page is first used. Some pages will be used again during the course of the year.

Unit 8: Fractions

Unit 9: Multiplication and Division

Unit 10: Measurement

Unit 11: Probability; End-of-Year Review

Activity Sheets

Product Patterns

Math Message

Complete the facts. Do not use the Multiplication/Division Facts Table.

1. $1 \times 1 =$ _____

2. $2 \times 2 =$ _____

3. $3 \times 3 =$ _____

4. $4 \times 4 =$ _____

5. $5 \times 5 =$ _____

6. $6 \times 6 =$ _____

7. $7 \times 7 =$ _____

8. $8 \times 8 =$ _____

9. $9 \times 9 =$ _____

10. $10 \times 10 =$ _____

A Two's Product Pattern

Multiply. Look for patterns.

11. $2 \times 2 =$ _____

12. $2 \times 2 \times 2 =$ _____

13. $2 \times 2 \times 2 \times 2 =$ _____

14. $2 \times 2 \times 2 \times 2 \times 2 =$ _____

15. $2 \times 2 \times 2 \times 2 \times 2 \times 2 =$ _____

Challenge

Use the Two's Product Pattern for Problems 11–15. Multiply.

16. $2 \times 2 \times 2 \times 2 \times 2 \times 2 \times 2 =$ _____

1. Name some items that are shaped like a cone.

_____

_____

Name some items that are shaped like a cylinder.

_____

_____

SRB
107

2. In the number 5,627,043:
the 4 means

4 tens

_____

the 6 means

_____

the 7 means

_____

the 5 means

_____

SRB
18–21

3. Use the "about 3 times" circle rule: For any circle, the circumference is about 3 times the diameter.

diameter	circumference
	24 cm
9 cm	
	21 cm

SRB
134 135

4. Use your calculator.

Enter	Change to	How?
469	1,469	_____
1,059	859	_____
23,672	23,972	_____
46,555	55,555	_____

SRB
18   19

5. What number is 90 more than 487?

_____

What number is 357 less than 608?

_____

SRB
51–57

6. 7 baskets. 9 apples per basket. How many apples in all?

_____ apples

8 cakes. 8 candles per cake. How many candles in all?

_____ candles

SRB
65 66

Multiplication/Division Facts Table

×, ÷	1	2	3	4	5	6	7	8	9	10
1	1	2	3	4	5	6	7	8	9	10
2	2	4	6	8	10	12	14	16	18	20
3	3	6	9	12	15	18	21	24	27	30
4	4	8	12	16	20	24	28	32	36	40
5	5	10	15	20	25	30	35	40	45	50
6	6	12	18	24	30	36	42	48	54	60
7	7	14	21	28	35	42	49	56	63	70
8	8	16	24	32	40	48	56	64	72	80
9	9	18	27	36	45	54	63	72	81	90
10	10	20	30	40	50	60	70	80	90	100

1. Draw the lines of symmetry.

There are _____ lines of symmetry.

2. The degree measure of the angle is:

○ less than 90°

○ less than 180°

○ more than 180°

○ 160°

3. Solve. Use multiplication doubles.

Unit
stickers

$6 \times 6 =$ _____

$7 \times 7 =$ _____

$8 \times 8 =$ _____

$81 =$ _____ $\times$ _____

$100 =$ _____ $\times$ _____

4. Write the number that has

9 in the thousandths place

7 in the ones place

3 in the tenths place

6 in the hundredths place

_____ . _____ _____ _____

5. Figure out this riddle.

I have four sides. My opposite sides are equal in length. I have two pairs of parallel sides. I do not have any right angles.

What shape am I?

_____

6. Rectangle *HFCD* is a(n)

_____ -by- _____ rectangle.

The area of rectangle *HFCD*:

_____ $\times$ _____ = _____ square units.

Multiplication Bingo

Read the rules for *Multiplication Bingo* on pages 218 and 219 in the *Student Reference Book.*

Write the list of numbers on each grid below.

List of numbers

1	9	18	30
4	12	20	36
6	15	24	50
8	16	25	100

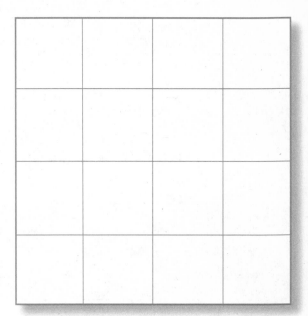

Record the facts you miss.
Practice them in your spare time.

_____

_____

_____

_____

_____

_____

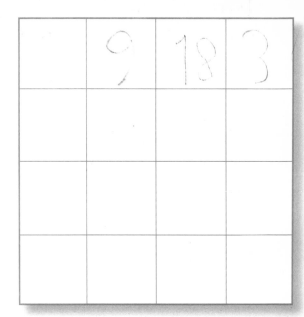

Multiplication/Division Practice

Fill in the missing number in each Fact Triangle.
Then write the fact family for the triangle.

1.

_____

_____

_____

_____

2.

_____

_____

_____

_____

Complete each puzzle.

Example

×,÷	3	5
4	*12*	*20*
6	*18*	*30*

3.

×,÷	2	6
3		
6		

4.

×,÷	3	5
2		
8		

5.

×,÷	7	9
2		
5		

6.

×,÷		4
3	9	
4		

7.

×,÷		6
2		
	24	36

Math Boxes 7.3

1. This is a picture of a cube. What do you know about this shape?

_____

_____

_____

_____ SRB 102–104

2. In the number 5,431,098:

the 3 means

_____ *thirty thousand* _____

the 4 means

_____

the 9 means _____

the 5 means _____

the 1 means

_____ SRB 19

3. Fill in the unit box. Then multiply.

Unit

$8 \times 2 =$ _____

$4 \times 9 =$ _____

$6 \times 7 =$ _____

_____ $= 8 \times 9$

_____ $= 7 \times 8$ SRB 46 47

4. Draw and label a pair of parallel lines. Draw and label a pair of intersecting rays.

 SRB 91

5. Add.

```
  349        777       2,765
+ 956     + 1,028    + 3,842
```

 SRB 51–53

6. Maxwell has $806 in the bank. Madison has $589. How much more money does Maxwell have than Madison?

$ _____

 SRB 190

Number Models with Parentheses

Solve the number story. Then write a number model using parentheses.

1. Amy scored 12 points and Yosh scored 6 points.
   If their team scored 41 points, how many points
   did the rest of the team score?

   _____

   Number model: _____

2. In a partner game, Tim has 10 points and Ellen
   14 points. They need 50 points to finish the game.
   How many more points are needed?

   _____

   Number model: _____

3. Once Tim and Ellen got 50 points, but lost
   14 points for a wrong move. They gained
   10 points back. What was their final score?

   _____

   Number model: _____

Add parentheses to complete the number models.

4. $20 - 10 + 4 = 6$

5. $20 - 10 + 4 = 14$

6. $100 - 21 + 10 = 69$

7. $100 - 21 + 10 = 89$

8. $27 - 8 + 3 = 22$

9. $18 = 6 + 3 \times 4$

10. $5 \times 9 - 2 = 35$

11. $51 = 43 + 15 - 7$

Complete these number models.

12. _____ $= 8 + (9 \times 3)$

13. $(75 - 29) + 5 =$ _____

14. $36 + (15 \div 3) =$ _____

15. _____ $= (8 \times 8) - 16$

Use with Lesson 7.4.

Math Boxes 7.4

1. Fill in the blanks for this ×,÷ puzzle.

×, ÷	5	
8		
	45	63

2. Subtract.

$$\begin{array}{r} 926 \\ -\ 538 \\ \hline \end{array} \quad \begin{array}{r} 1,045 \\ -\ 471 \\ \hline \end{array} \quad \begin{array}{r} 4,531 \\ -\ 2,628 \\ \hline \end{array}$$

54–57

3. Solve.

$49 \div 7 =$ _____

$81 \div 9 =$ _____

_____ $= 64 \div 8$

$6 = 36 \div$ _____

_____ $\div 5 = 5$

46 47

4. 1st grade collected 545 pop cans.

2nd grade collected 766 pop cans.

3rd grade collected 802 pop cans.

How many in all?

_____ pop cans

188 189

5. Draw a parallelogram. Label the vertices so that $\overline{AB} \parallel \overline{CD}$. The symbol ∥ means "is parallel to."

98 99

6. How many children like green? _____ children
How many children in all responded to the question? _____ children

Favorite Color	Number of Children
blue	ﬀﬀ ﬀﬀ
red	ﬀﬀ III
green	ﬀﬀ ﬀﬀ I
other	ﬀﬀ ﬀﬀ IIII

SRB
70–72

Scoring 10 Basketball Points

Find different ways to score 10 points in a basketball game.

Number of 3-point baskets	Number of 2-point baskets	Number of 1-point baskets	Number models
2	2	0	$(2 \times 3) + (2 \times 2) + (0 \times 1) = 10$

Use with Lesson 7.5.

Multiplication and Division Practice

Fill in the missing number in each Fact Triangle.
Then write the fact family for the triangle.

1.

_____

_____

_____

_____

2.

_____

_____

_____

_____

3.

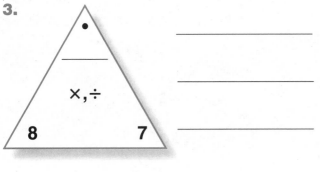

_____

_____

_____

_____

4.

_____

_____

_____

_____

5. Circle the Fact Triangle above that shows a square product.

Fill in the tables and find the missing rule.

6.

in	out
3	24
7	56
8	
4	
	72

7.

in
Rule
out

in	out
5	45
8	72
9	
	27
	36

Math Boxes 7.5

1. This drawing shows a rectangular prism.

How many faces does

it have? _____ faces

How many edges? _____ edges

How many vertices? _____ vertices

SRB
102–104

2. Write the number that has

9 in the ten-thousands place

4 in the millions place

2 in the hundreds place

5 in the thousands place

0 in all of the other places

___ , ___ ___ ___ , ___ ___ ___

SRB
18–21

3. Solve.

Unit
chairs

$8 \times 4 =$ _____

$9 \times 2 =$ _____

_____ $= 7 \times 8$

$4 \times 9 =$ _____

$6 \times 8 =$ _____

SRB
46   47

4. The degree measure of the angle is

○ less than 40°

○ more than 100°

○ more than 180°

○ 90°

SRB
149 150

5. Fill in the unit box. Then solve.

Unit

$(6 \times 3) + 2 =$ _____

$29 - (20 + 3) =$ _____

_____ $= 14 + (3 + 3)$

_____ $= (5 \times 5) - 6$

SRB
16   17

6. Forty markers are divided equally into 8 packages.

How many markers are

in each package? _____ markers

How many markers are

left over? _____ markers

SRB
65   66

Extended Multiplication and Division Facts

Write the number of 3s in each each number.

1. How many 3s in 30? _____
2. How many 3s in 300? _____
3. How many 3s in 3,000? _____
4. How many 3s in 12? _____
5. How many 3s in 120? _____
6. How many 3s in 1,200? _____

Solve each ×, ÷ puzzle. Fill in the blanks.

Example

×, ÷	300	2,000
2	600	4,000
3	900	6,000

7.

×, ÷	60	300
4		
5	300	

8.

×, ÷	4	5
200		
8,000		

9.

×, ÷		1,000
3	1,500	
		6,000

Solve each number story.

10. A 30-minute television program has two 60-second commercials at the beginning and two at the end. There are also four 30-second commercials in the middle of the program. How long is the actual program?

    _____ minutes

11. During a 40-minute basketball game, each team is allowed four 60-second timeouts and two 30-second timeouts. If both teams use all of their timeouts, how many minutes of timeouts will there be?

    _____ minutes

Math Boxes 7.6

1. Write in the missing numbers.

×, ÷		6
8		
	27	54

2. Give two reasons that this shape is a regular polygon.

_____

_____

_____

_____

_____

_____

3. Solve. Use multiplication doubles.

Unit
stickers

$5 \times 5 =$ _____

_____ $= 7 \times 7$

_____ $= 9 \times 9$

$8 \times 8 =$ _____

$6 \times 6 =$ _____

4. Draw and label 3 parallel line segments. Draw and label a line that intersects all 3 line segments.

5. Draw the lines of symmetry.

There are _____ lines of symmetry.

6. In the number 42.368:

the 3 means ___0.3___

the 2 means _____

the 8 means _____

the 6 means _____

the 4 means _____

Stock-Up Sale Record

Use the items on pages 240 and 241 in your *Student Reference Book*.

Round 1:

Item to be purchased: _____

How many? _____

Regular or sale price? _____

Price per item: _____

Estimated cost: _____

Round 2:

Item to be purchased: _____

How many? _____

Regular or sale price? _____

Price per item: _____

Estimated cost: _____

Round 3:

Item to be purchased: _____

How many? _____

Regular or sale price? _____

Price per item: _____

Estimated cost: _____

Round 4:

Item to be purchased: _____

How many? _____

Regular or sale price? _____

Price per item: _____

Estimated cost: _____

Round 5:

Item to be purchased: _____

How many? _____

Regular or sale price? _____

Price per item: _____

Estimated cost: _____

Round 6:

Item to be purchased: _____

How many? _____

Regular or sale price? _____

Price per item: _____

Estimated cost: _____

Extended Facts Practice

Solve the calculator puzzles. Use the ⊗ or ⊘ for each puzzle.

	Enter	Change to	How?
1.	10	1,000	_____
2.	1,000	100	_____
3.	100	10,000	_____
4.	1,000	10	_____
5.	10,000	1,000	_____

6. Three of the names do not belong in this name-collection box. Cross them out.

4,000

$8 \times 5{,}000$	$(500 \times 5) - 500$
$5{,}000 - (5 \times 200)$	
$(200 \times 4) \times 5$	
$(200 \div 4) \times 8$	
$8{,}000 \div 2$	$(2 \times 2) \times 1000$
$(200 + 200) \times 10$	
$2 \times 2{,}000$	$1{,}000 \times 4$

Complete the extended Fact Triangles. Write the extended fact families.

7.

8.

_____

_____

_____

_____

Solve each ×, ÷ puzzle. Fill in the blanks.

9.

×, ÷	3	9
100		900
3,000		

10.

×, ÷		2,000
4	1,200	
		10,000

1. square pyramid

How many faces does it have?

_____ faces

How many edges? _____ edges

How many vertices? _____ vertices

What is the shape of the base?

_____

SRB 105

2. Write the number that has

3 in the hundred-thousands place

6 in the thousands place

4 in the ten-thousands place

1 in the millions place

5 in all of the other places

__ , __ __ __ , __ __ __

SRB 18–21

3. Solve.
Fill in the unit box.

Unit

$6 \times 9 =$ _____

_____ $= 9 \times 8$

_____ $= 6 \times 7$

_____ $= 5 \times 8$

$9 \times 7 =$ _____

SRB 46 47

4. Solve.

Unit
stones

$4 \times 8 =$ _____

$4 \times 80 =$ _____

$4 \times 800 =$ _____

$4 \times 8,000 =$ _____

5. Complete the number models.

$(49 - 19) - 8 =$ _____

$(56 - 14) \times 2 =$ _____

$48 - (19 - 8) =$ _____

$56 - (14 - 2) =$ _____

SRB 16 17

6. Wilson had 493 coins in his collection. He sold 237 of them. How many coins does Wilson have now?

_____ coins

SRB 186 187

Tens Times Tens

Math Message

Write the dollar values.

1.   10 $10 = $_____

2.   100 $10 = $_____

3. 1,000 $10 = $_____

4.   10 $100 = $_____

5.   100 $100 = $_____

6. 1,000 $100 = $_____

Solve each ×, ÷ puzzle. Fill in the blanks.

7.

×, ÷	10	100
1		
10		

8.

×, ÷	4	30
20		
6		

9.

×, ÷	40	60
20		
80		

10.

×, ÷		
3	150	
70		560

Multiply.

11. 5 × 90 = _____

12. _____ = 70 × 4

13. 10 × 70 = _____

14. 80 × 60 = _____

15. _____ = 30 × 50

16. 7 × _____ = 420

17. _____ × 90 = 540

18. _____ × 600 = 6,000

Challenge

19. No calculators, please! An artist made a
square mosaic with 99 rows of tiles and
99 tiles in each row. How many tiles were used? _____

                                                            (unit)

1. Fill in the blanks for this ×,÷ puzzle.

×,÷	9	6
7		
9		

2. Multiply.

$$\begin{array}{r} 5 \\ \times\ 9 \\ \hline \end{array} \qquad \begin{array}{r} 50 \\ \times\ 9 \\ \hline \end{array} \qquad \begin{array}{r} 500 \\ \times\ 9 \\ \hline \end{array}$$

$$\begin{array}{r} 3 \\ \times\ 9 \\ \hline \end{array} \qquad \begin{array}{r} 30 \\ \times\ 9 \\ \hline \end{array} \qquad \begin{array}{r} 300 \\ \times\ 9 \\ \hline \end{array}$$

3. Write multiplication names for three different square numbers.

_____

_____

_____

4. The best estimate of 5,697 + 1,310 is:

0 about 8,100

0 about 8,000

0 about 7,000

0 about 5,901

5. Add parentheses to complete the number models.

30 = 10 × 2 + 10

46 − 23 − 13 = 10

4 ÷ 2 + 6 = 8

6. Draw an angle that measures between 90° and 180°.

Math Boxes 7.9

1. Number of pets children have:

0, 4, 0, 1, 1, 3, 6, 2, 5

Median: _____

Maximum: _____

Minimum: _____

Range: _____

2. Solve.

$7 \times 8 =$ _____

$7 \times 80 =$ _____

_____ $= 70 \times 80$

$70 \times 8,000 =$ _____

3. Solve. Fill in the unit box.

Unit

$4 \times 9 =$ _____

$2 \times 8 =$ _____

_____ $= 6 \times 7$

_____ $= 5 \times 8$

_____ $= 6 \times 9$

4. The best estimate of $3,465 + 2,988$ is:

O about 5,000

O about 6,000

O about 6,500

O about 7,000

5. Add parentheses to complete the number models.

$14 - 7 \times 2 = 14$

$3 \times 6 + 2 = 24$

$7 = 6 + 15 \div 3$

$9 \times 5 + 3 = 72$

6. Draw a ray, $\vec{AB}$, that is parallel to the line, $\overleftrightarrow{CD}$, and intersects the line segment, $\overline{EF}$.

Use with Lesson 7.9.

Math Boxes 7.10

1. Circle the pictures in which $\frac{1}{2}$ is shaded.

2. Divide each figure into 4 equal parts.

3. True or false?

$\frac{1}{3}$ of the squares are shaded.

_____

4. Divide the triangles into 3 equal groups.

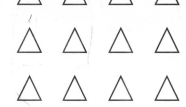

5. Shade $\frac{1}{2}$ of the hexagon.

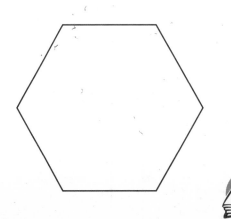

6. Shade $\frac{1}{2}$ of the balloons.

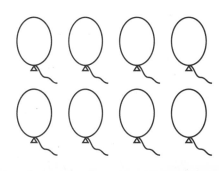

Fraction Review

Math Message

1. Draw an X through $\frac{2}{3}$ of the circles.

Label each picture with one of the following numbers: $0, \frac{0}{4}, \frac{1}{4}, \frac{1}{2}, \frac{2}{4},$ or $\frac{3}{4}$.

   2.   3.   4.   5.

$\frac{4}{4}$, or 1   _____   _____   _____   _____

Each whole figure represents ONE.
Write a fraction that names each region inside the figure.

6.   7.   8.

9.   10.   11.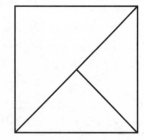

Challenge

Each whole figure represents ONE.
Write a fraction that names each region inside the figure.

12.   13.

Fraction Review (cont.)

You need at least 25 pennies or other counters. Use them to help you solve these problems. Share solution strategies with others in your group.

Unit
counters

Make a set of 8 counters.

14. Show $\frac{1}{4}$ of a set of 8 counters. How many counters is that?

_____

15. Put the counters back. Show $\frac{2}{4}$ of the set. How many counters?

_____

16. Put the counters back. Show $\frac{3}{4}$ of the set. How many counters?

_____

Make a set of 12 counters.

17. Show $\frac{1}{3}$ of the set. How many counters is that?

_____

18. Put the counters back. Show $\frac{2}{3}$ of the set. How many counters?

_____

19. Put the counters back. Show $\frac{3}{3}$ of the set. How many counters?

_____

20. Show $\frac{1}{5}$ of a set of 15 counters. How many counters is that?

_____

21. Show $\frac{4}{5}$ of a set of 15 counters. How many counters is that?

_____

22. Show $\frac{3}{4}$ of a set of 20 counters. How many counters is that?

_____

23. Show $\frac{2}{3}$ of a set of 18 counters. How many counters?

_____

24. Five counters is $\frac{1}{5}$ of a set. How many are in the whole set?

_____

25. Six counters is $\frac{1}{3}$ of a set. How many are in the whole set?

_____

Challenge

26. Twelve counters is $\frac{3}{4}$ of a set. How many are in the complete set of counters? _____

27. Pretend that you have 15 "cheese cubes" that can be cut. How many are in $\frac{1}{2}$ of the set of cubes? Use a fraction or decimal in your answer. _____

Math Boxes 8.1

1. The "about 3 times" circle rule: For any circle, the circumference is about 3 times the diameter.

Unit
cm

Diameter	Circumference
8	
80	
800	

2. Solve. Fill in the unit box.

Unit

$6 \times 8 =$ _____

$9 \times 9 =$ _____

$7 \times 7 =$ _____

_____ $= 8 \times 9$

_____ $= 4 \times 8$

3.
```
   6,709
+    844
```

Write a number model for your estimate.

_____ + _____ = _____

Answer: _____

4. In the number 3.514:

the 3 means ___ *3 ones* ___

the 1 means _____

the 5 means _____

the 4 means _____

5. Complete the number grid puzzle.

874

6. Fill in the rule box and the frames.

+ 7

920

930

Fractions with Pattern Blocks

Work with a partner.

Materials   ☐ pattern blocks
               ☐ Pattern-Block Template

Part 1

Cover each shape with green △ pattern blocks. What fractional part of each shape is 1 green pattern block? Write the fraction under each shape.

  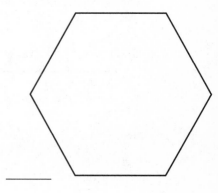

Part 2

Cover each shape with green △ pattern blocks. What fractional part of each shape are 2 green pattern blocks? Write the fraction next to each shape.

Fractions with Pattern Blocks (cont.)

Part 3

Cover each shape with blue 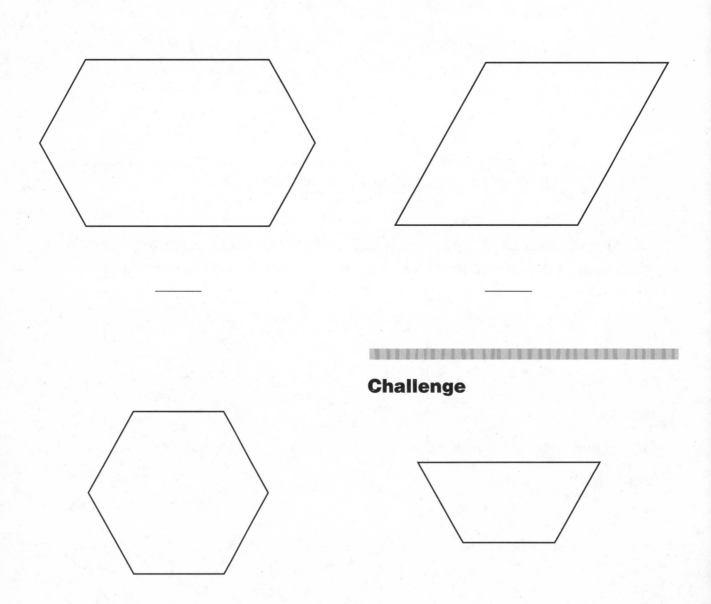 pattern blocks. What fractional part of each shape is 1 blue pattern block? Write the fraction under each shape. If you can't cover the whole shape, cover as much as you can. *Think:* Is there another block that would cover the rest of the shape?

_____   _____

Challenge

_____   _____

Fractions with Pattern Blocks (cont.)

Part 4

Cover each shape with blue ◇ pattern blocks. What fractional part of each shape would 2 blue pattern blocks cover? Write the fraction next to each shape.

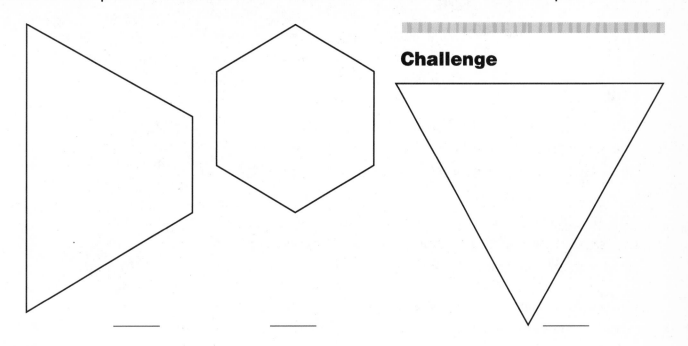

Challenge

Part 5

Use your Pattern-Block Template to show how you divided the shapes in each section. *Remember:* The number *under* the fraction bar names the number of equal parts into which the whole shape is divided.

Follow-Up

Get together with the rest of the group.

- Compare your answers.
- Use the blocks to check your answers.
- Can more than one fraction be correct?

Dressing for the Party

Work in a group of four.

Materials
- ❏ *Math Masters,* p. 129 (Pants and Socks Cutouts)
- ❏ scissors
- ❏ tape
- ❏ blue, red, green, and black crayons or coloring pencils

Problem

Pretend that you have 4 pairs of pants: blue, red, green, and black. You also have 4 pairs of socks: blue, red, green, and black. You have been invited to a party. You need to choose a pair of pants and a pair of socks to wear. Of course, both socks must be the same color. For example, the pants could be blue and both socks black.

How many different combinations of these pants and socks are possible?

Strategy

Use the cutouts on *Math Masters,* page 129, and crayons to help you answer the question.

Decide on a good way for your group to share the following work before you start to answer the question.

- Color the pants in the first row blue.
- Color the pants in the second row red.
- Color the pants in the third row green and those in the fourth row black.
- Color the socks in the same way.
- Cut out each pair of pants and each pair of socks.
- Tape together pairs of pants and pairs of socks to show different outfits. Check that you have only one of each outfit.

Dressing for the Party (cont.)   189

Pretend that you have 4 different colors of pants and 4 different colors of socks.

1. How many different combinations of
    pants and socks did your group find? _____

2. Is this all of the possible combinations? _____

3. How do you know?

    _____

    _____

    _____

    _____

4. How did your group divide up the work?

    _____

    _____

    _____

5. How did your group solve the problem?

    _____

    _____

    _____

    _____

1. Circle $\frac{5}{10}$ of the collection of triangles.

Name the fraction that is left in 2 ways.

_____ and _____

24

2. Number of children per classroom:

25, 30, 26, 28, 33, 35, 28

Median: _____

Maximum: _____

Minimum: _____

Range: _____

73 74

3. Put in the parentheses needed to complete the number models.

$31 = 3 + 7 \times 4$

$40 = 3 + 7 \times 4$

$4 \times 8 + 2 \times 2 = 36$

$4 \times 8 + 2 \times 2 = 80$

16 17

4. Subtract.

$$\begin{array}{r} 439 \\ -\ 378 \\ \hline \end{array} \qquad \begin{array}{r} 4{,}666 \\ -\ 1{,}297 \\ \hline \end{array} \qquad \begin{array}{r} 3{,}408 \\ -\ 571 \\ \hline \end{array}$$

SRB
54 55

5. Fill in the missing numbers.

×, ÷	700	60
8		
	4,900	

6. Complete.

24 inches = _____ feet

30 cm = _____ mm

_____ yards = 12 feet

_____ yards = 72 inches

4 meters = _____ centimeters

122
128 129

Fraction Number-Line Poster

1 Whole

Halves

Fourths

Eighths

Thirds

Sixths

1. Shade $\frac{3}{8}$ of the circle.

What fraction is *un*shaded? _____

2. Fill in the missing numbers.

×, ÷	4	9
	28	
8		72

3. Measure the line segment to the nearest $\frac{1}{4}$ inch.

_____

_____

Draw a line segment $1\frac{3}{4}$ inches long.

4. Circle the digit in the millions place.

Put an X on the digit in the ten-thousands place.

Put a box around the digit in the hundreds place.

4 , 9 0 2 , 5 6 7

5. Draw an angle that measures between 5° and 90°.

6. Write a definition for *parallel*.

_____

_____

_____

_____

Write a definition for *intersect*.

_____

_____

Table of Equivalent Fractions

Use your deck of Fraction Cards to find equivalent fractions.
Record them in the table.

Fraction	Equivalent Fractions
$\frac{0}{2}$	
$\frac{1}{2}$	
$\frac{2}{2}$	
$\frac{1}{3}$	
$\frac{2}{3}$	
$\frac{1}{4}$	
$\frac{3}{4}$	
$\frac{1}{5}$	
$\frac{4}{5}$	
$\frac{1}{6}$	
$\frac{5}{6}$	

Challenge

Fraction	Equivalent Fractions
$\frac{1}{8}$	
$\frac{5}{8}$	
$\frac{2}{9}$	

Use with Lessons 8.4 and 8.5.

Fractions of Sets

What fraction does each picture show? Shade the oval next to each correct answer. There may be more than one correct answer.

1.

○ $\frac{1}{4}$ ○ $\frac{1}{2}$

○ $\frac{2}{3}$ ○ $\frac{6}{6}$

2.

○ $\frac{1}{4}$ ○ $\frac{3}{6}$

○ $\frac{6}{6}$ ○ $\frac{3}{4}$

3.

○ $\frac{1}{2}$ ○ $\frac{6}{1}$

○ $\frac{1}{6}$ ○ $\frac{6}{6}$

4.

○ $\frac{4}{6}$ ○ $\frac{1}{4}$

○ $\frac{6}{6}$ ○ $\frac{2}{3}$

5.

○ $\frac{0}{4}$ ○ $\frac{3}{4}$

○ $\frac{1}{2}$ ○ $\frac{1}{4}$

6.

○ $\frac{0}{4}$ ○ $\frac{3}{4}$

○ $\frac{1}{2}$ ○ $\frac{1}{4}$

7.

○ $\frac{0}{4}$ ○ $\frac{3}{4}$

○ $\frac{1}{2}$ ○ $\frac{1}{4}$

8.

○ $\frac{0}{4}$ ○ $\frac{3}{4}$

○ $\frac{1}{2}$ ○ $\frac{1}{4}$

Challenge

9.

○ $\frac{1}{4}$ ○ $\frac{1}{2}$

○ $\frac{2}{12}$ ○ $\frac{2}{3}$

10.

○ $\frac{3}{4}$ ○ $\frac{3}{6}$

○ $\frac{12}{12}$ ○ $\frac{6}{12}$

11.

○ $\frac{3}{4}$ ○ $\frac{12}{1}$

○ $\frac{12}{12}$ ○ $\frac{0}{12}$

12.

○ $\frac{1}{2}$ ○ $\frac{12}{12}$

○ $\frac{8}{12}$ ○ $\frac{3}{4}$

Time

Math Boxes 8.4

1. Shade $\frac{7}{10}$ of the hats.

SRB
24

2.
$$\begin{array}{r} 3,333 \\ +\quad 999 \\ \hline \end{array}$$

Write a number model
for your estimate.

_____ + _____ = _____

Answer: _____

SRB
51 52
168

3. Fill in the missing numbers.
Use fractions.

0          $\frac{1}{2}$ 1

_____   _____

4. Write <, >, or =.

0.75 ☐ 0.57

0.09 ☐ 0.9

0.062 ☐ 0.107

12.4 ☐ 14.2

SRB
36

5. Fill in the missing numbers.

×, ÷		600
50	1,500	
		42,000

6. Measure the line segment to the
nearest $\frac{1}{4}$ inch.

_____

_____

Draw a line segment 1 inch long.

SRB
125 126

Color the Fraction Cat

Color the picture below. Follow the color key. For example, all parts with a fraction equivalent to $\frac{2}{3}$ should be colored orange. So the part with $\frac{4}{6}$ should also be colored orange.

Fractions Equal To	Color Key
$\frac{1}{2}$	yellow
$\frac{2}{3}$	orange
$\frac{1}{3}$	brown
$\frac{1}{4}$	green
$\frac{3}{4}$	black

Use with Lesson 8.5.

Math Boxes 8.5

1. Color $\frac{2}{5}$ of the rectangle.

What fraction is *un*colored? _____

2. Solve.

Unit
stamps

$54 \div 9 =$ _____

$27 \div 3 =$ _____

_____ $= 36 \div 6$

_____ $= 64 \div 8$

$45 \div 5 =$ _____

3. Fill in the missing numbers.
Use fractions.

0         $\frac{2}{3}$

_____   _____   _____

4. Complete the
number models.

Unit
books

$(4 + 3) - 2 =$ _____

$10 = 6 + (2 +$ _____ $)$

_____ $= 3 \times (9 - 0)$

$(5 \times 5) - 4 =$ _____

5. Write 4 fractions equivalent to $\frac{1}{2}$.

_____   _____

_____   _____

6. Subtract.

6,000	801	3,411
− 583	− 472	− 2,862

More Than ONE

Use the circles that you cut out for the Math Message.

1. Glue 3 halves into the two whole circles.

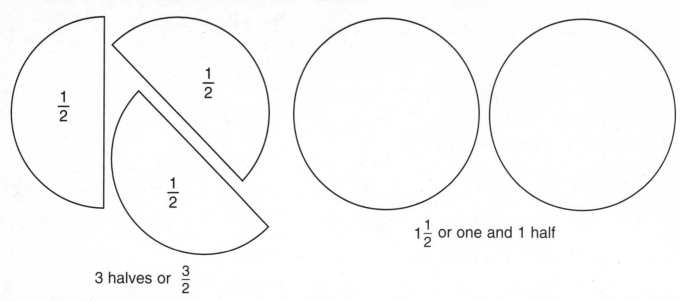

3 halves or $\frac{3}{2}$

$1\frac{1}{2}$ or one and 1 half

2. Glue 6 fourths into the two whole circles. Fill in the missing digits in the question, the fraction, and the mixed number.

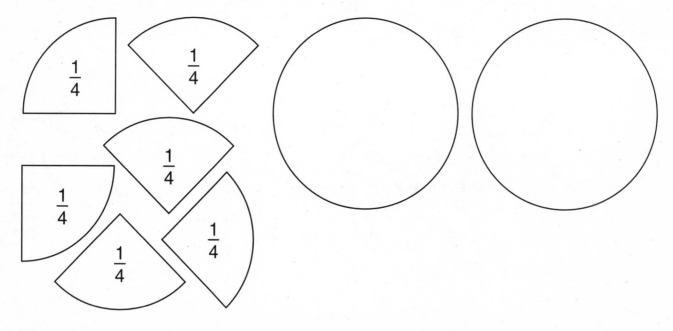

How many fourths? _____ fourths

Write the fraction $\dfrac{}{}$

Write the mixed number: $1\dfrac{}{}$

Use with Lesson 8.6.

More Than ONE (cont.)

3.

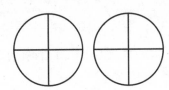

How many fourths? _____ fourths

Write the fraction ▢/▢

Color 5 fourths.

Write the mixed number: 1 ▢/▢

4.

How many thirds? _____ thirds

Write the fraction: ▢/▢

Color 5 thirds.

Write the mixed number: 1 ▢/▢

5.

How many fifths? _____ fifths

Write the fraction: ▢/▢

Color 8 fifths.

Write the mixed number: ▢ ▢/▢

6.

How many thirds? _____ thirds

Write the fraction: ▢/▢

Color 8 thirds.

Write the mixed number: ▢ ▢/▢

Math Boxes 8.6

1. Draw a set of 12 Xs. Circle 9 of them. What fraction of the whole set are the 9 Xs?

_____

SRB
24

2. Fill in the oval next to the best estimate.

$589 + 2,115 =$ _____

○ about 2,000

○ about 2,500

○ about 2,200

○ about 2,700

SRB
168

3. Write four fractions greater than $\frac{1}{3}$.

_____   _____

_____   _____

4. Complete the bar graph.

Kate swam 5 laps.

Jen swam 3 laps.

Marc swam 6 laps.

Median number of laps: _____

SRB
78
80 81

5. Write 4 fractions equivalent to $\frac{1}{4}$.

_____   _____

_____   _____

SRB
30

6. Fill in the missing factor.

$6 \times$ _____ $= 3,600$

$8 \times$ _____ $= 16,000$

$9 \times$ _____ $= 720$

$2 \times$ _____ $= 1,800$

Use with Lesson 8.6.

Fraction Number Stories

Solve these number stories. Use pennies or counters, or draw pictures to help you.

1. There are 8 apples in the package. Glenn did not eat any. What fraction of the package did Glenn eat?

_____

2. Anik bought a dozen eggs at the supermarket. When he got home, he found that $\frac{1}{6}$ of the eggs were cracked. How many eggs were cracked?

_____ eggs

3. Chante used $\frac{2}{3}$ of a package of ribbon to wrap presents. Did she use more or less than $\frac{3}{4}$ of the package?

_____

4. I had 2 whole cookies. I gave you $\frac{1}{4}$ of 1 cookie. How many cookies did I have left?

_____ cookies

5. There are 10 quarters. You have 3. I have 2. What fraction of the quarters do you have?

_____

What fraction of the quarters do I have?

_____

What fraction of the quarters do we have together?

_____

6. One day, Edwin read $\frac{1}{3}$ of a book. The next day, he read another $\frac{1}{3}$ of the book. What fraction of the book had he read after 2 days?

_____

What fraction of the book did he have left to read?

_____

7. Dorothy walks $1\frac{1}{2}$ miles to school. Jaime walks $1\frac{2}{4}$ miles to school. Who walks the longer distance?

_____

_____

8. Twelve children shared 2 medium-size pizzas equally. What fraction of 1 whole pizza did each child eat?

_____

Fraction Number Stories (cont.)

9. Write a fraction story. Ask your partner to solve it.

_____

_____

_____

_____

_____

Draw eggs in each carton to show the fraction.

Example $\frac{7}{12}$

10. $\frac{6}{12}$

11. $\frac{3}{4}$

12. $\frac{4}{12}$

13. $\frac{1}{3}$

14. $\frac{3}{12}$

15. $\frac{1}{2}$

16. Julie drank $\frac{1}{4}$ of a glass of juice.

Draw an empty glass.

Shade in the glass to show how much juice is left.

           Use with Lesson 8.7.

1. Color $\frac{6}{8}$ of the circle.

What fraction is *un*shaded?

_____

 SRB 22 23

2. Write <, >, or =.

$\frac{3}{4}$ ☐ $\frac{1}{4}$ $\frac{1}{4}$ ☐ $\frac{2}{8}$

$\frac{3}{8}$ ☐ $\frac{7}{8}$ $\frac{5}{6}$ ☐ $\frac{1}{6}$

$\frac{5}{10}$ ☐ $\frac{1}{2}$

 SRB 30 31

3. Fill in the missing numbers on the number line.

0        $\frac{1}{5}$

____ ____ ____

4. How many thirds are shaded?

_____ thirds

Write the fraction: _____

5. Circle the fractions that are equivalent to $\frac{1}{3}$.

$\frac{1}{8}$ $\frac{2}{6}$ $\frac{4}{12}$

$\frac{6}{9}$ $\frac{5}{15}$ $\frac{3}{9}$

SRB 30

6. Solve. Fill in the unit box.

Unit

$4 \times 9 =$

$8 \times 8 =$ _____

 $= 5 \times 8$

_____ $= 7 \times 9$

 $= 6 \times 6$

 SRB 46 47

Math Boxes 8.8

1. Solve.

$5 \times 9 =$ _____

$5 \times 90 =$ _____

$5 \times 900 =$ _____

_____ $= 3 \times 8$

_____ $= 30 \times 80$

_____ $= 300 \times 80$

2. Share $3.75 equally among 3 people.

Each person gets $_____ .

Share $10.00 equally among 4 people.

Each person gets $_____ .

3. 30 is 10 times as much as _____.

500 is _____ times as much as 5.

_____ is 100 times as much as 80.

40,000 is 1,000 times as much as _____ .

4. 9 cups. 9 ice cubes per cup. How many ice cubes in all?

_____

3 packages. 9 juice boxes per package. How many juice boxes in all?

_____

5. Draw a 3-by-8 array of Xs.

How many Xs in all? _____

Write a number model.

_____

6. 9 children share 18 candies. How many candies per child?

_____

How many candies left over?

_____

16 books in all. 3 books per shelf.

How many shelves? _____

How many books left over? _____

Multiples of 10, 100, and 1,000

Solve each problem.

1. a. 7 [40s] = _____   b. $7 \times 40 =$ _____

2. a. 600 [20s] = _____   b. $600 \times 20 =$ _____

3. a. How many 3s are in 2,700? _____

   b. _____ $\times\ 3 = 2{,}700$ c. $2{,}700 \div 3 =$ _____

4. How many 50s are in 4,000? _____

5. How many 800s are in 2,400? _____

6. How many 70s are in 420? _____

7. a. $40 \times 300 =$ _____   b. $12{,}000 \div 40 =$ _____

For Problems 8–11, use the information on the next two journal pages.

8. a. Which animal might weigh about
   20 times as much as a 30-pound raccoon? _____

   b. Can you name two other animals which might
   weigh 20 times as much as a 30-pound raccoon?

   _____

9. About how many 200-pound American alligators
   weigh about as much as a 3,200-pound
   Beluga whale?   _____

Challenge

10. Which animal might weigh about 100 times
    as much as the combined weights of a
    15-pound Arctic fox and a 10-pound Arctic fox? _____

11. About how many $4\frac{1}{2}$-pound snowshoe hares
    weigh as much as a 27-pound porcupine?   _____

Use with Lesson 9.1.   (two hundred five) **205**

Adult Weights of North American Animals

Source: *Do Elephants Eat Too Much?* Robert Balfanz. Everyday Learning Corporation, 1992.

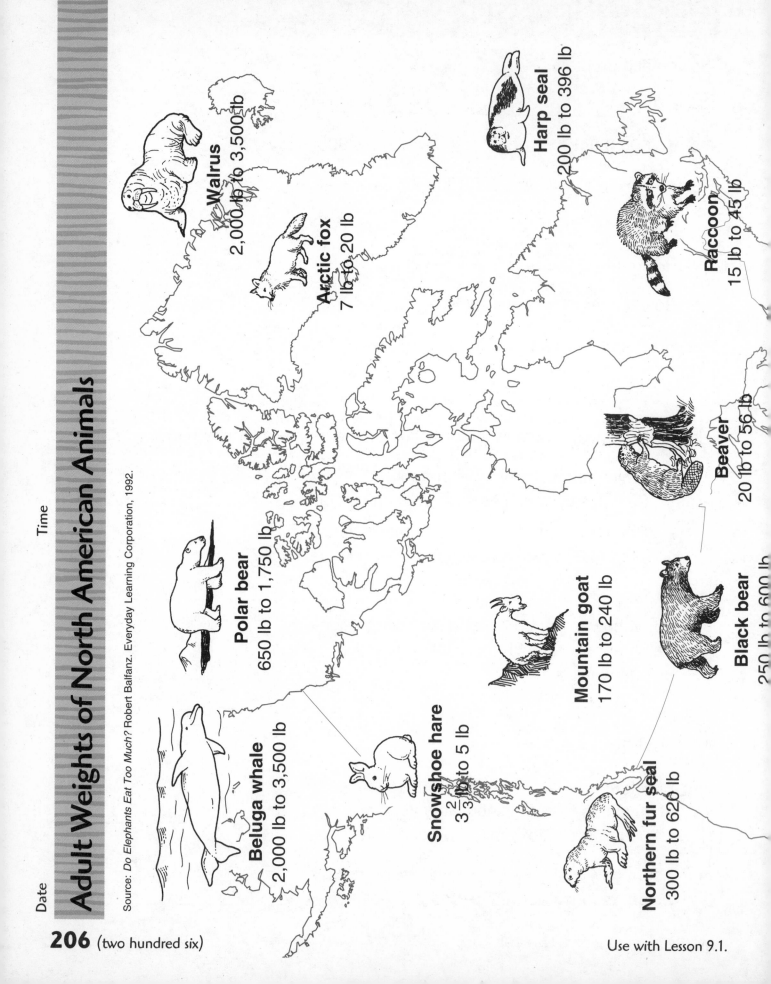

Walrus
2,000 lb to 3,500 lb

Arctic fox
7 lb to 20 lb

Harp seal
200 lb to 396 lb

Raccoon
15 lb to 45 lb

Beaver
20 lb to 56 lb

Polar bear
650 lb to 1,750 lb

Mountain goat
170 lb to 240 lb

Black bear
250 lb to 600 lb

Beluga whale
2,000 lb to 3,500 lb

Snowshoe hare
$3\frac{2}{3}$ lb to 5 lb

Northern fur seal
300 lb to 620 lb

Pilot whale
3,200 lb to 6,400 lb

Atlantic green turtle
250 lb to 450 lb

West Indian manatee
500 lb to 1,100 lb

American porcupine
20 lb to 40 lb

White-tailed deer
50 lb to 480 lb

American alligator
200 lb to 500 lb

Puma
150 lb to 230 lb

Gray fox
9 lb to 16 lb

Common dolphin
200 lb to 300 lb

Gila monster
2½ lb to 4 lb

Gray whale
45,000 lb to 72,000 lb

Sea otter
48 lb to 99 lb

Bottle-nosed dolphin
350 lb to 430 lb

Right whale
70,000 lb to 140,000 lb

Use with Lesson 9.1.

Number Stories

Use the Adult Weights of North American Animals poster on the previous pages. Make up multiplication and division animal number stories. Ask a partner to solve your number stories.

1. _____

_____

_____

_____

_____

Answer:_____

2. _____

_____

_____

_____

_____

Answer:_____

3. _____

_____

_____

_____

_____

Answer:_____

Math Boxes 9.1

1. Write 5 fractions greater than $\frac{1}{2}$.

_____, _____, _____, _____, _____

Write 5 fractions less than $\frac{1}{2}$.

_____, _____, _____, _____, _____

Write 3 other names for $\frac{1}{2}$.

_____, _____, _____

2. Show two ways a team can score 37 points in a football game.

7 points	6 points	3 points	2 points

3. How many fourths are shaded?

_____ fourths

Write the fraction: _____

Write the mixed number: _____ / _____

4. This shape is a _____.

It has _____ lines of symmetry.

Draw the lines of symmetry.

5. Complete.

a. 24, 30, _____, _____, 48, _____

b. _____, 56, 64, _____, _____

6. Draw an angle that measures between 0° and 90°.

Mental Multiplication

Solve these problems in your head. Use a slate and chalk, or pencil and paper, to help you keep track of your thinking. For some of the problems, you will need to use the information on journal pages 206 and 207.

1. Could 12 harp seals weigh more than 1 ton? _____ Less than 1 ton? _____

   Explain the strategy that you used.

   _____

   _____

   _____

2. How much do eight 53-pound white-tailed deer weigh? _____

   Explain the strategy that you used.

   _____

   _____

3. How much do six 87-pound sea otters weigh? _____

4. How much do seven 260-pound Atlantic green
   turtles weigh?   _____

5. $7 \times 23 =$ _____

6. _____ $= 8 \times 46$

7. _____ $= 4 \times 26$

8. $9 \times 32 =$ _____

9. $6 \times 54 =$ _____

10. _____ $= 3 \times 320$

11. $2 \times 460 =$ _____

12. _____ $= 4 \times 250$

Use with Lesson 9.2.

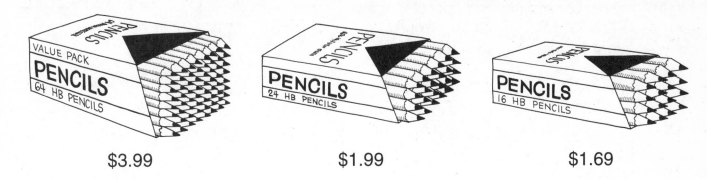

$3.99 $1.99 $1.69

Solve the following problems in your head. Use a slate or pencil and scratch paper to keep track of your thinking.

1. How many pencils are in two 24-pencil packages? _____

2. How many pencils are in three 16-pencil packages? _____

3. How much do two 24-pencil packages cost? _____

4. How much do three 16-pencil packages cost? _____

5. How much do you save if you buy two 24-pencil packages instead of three 16-pencil packages? _____

6. What is the total number of pencils in two 24-pencil packages and one 16-pencil package? _____

7. What is the total cost of two 24-pencil packages and one 16-pencil package? _____

8. How much do you save if you buy one 64-pencil package instead of two 24-pencil packages and one 16-pencil package? _____

9. Explain how you solved Problem 3 in your head.

_____

_____

_____

1. Anthony ate $\frac{3}{4}$ of his sandwich. What fraction of the sandwich

is left? _____

Justin ate $\frac{2}{3}$ of his sandwich. Did he eat more or less than $\frac{1}{2}$ of the sandwich?

_____

SRB 22 23 31

2. How many 10s in 40? _____

How many 10s in 100? _____

How many 10s in 160? _____

How many 10s in 210? _____

SRB 18 19

3. Draw two ways to show $\frac{2}{3}$.

SRB 22–24

4. Draw a line segment *AB* that is 2 inches long. Draw a line segment *CD* parallel to the first line.

SRB 88 91 125

5. 56.714

___6___ is in the ones place.

_____ is in the tenths place.

_____ is in the thousandths place.

_____ is in the tens place.

_____ is in the hundredths place.

SRB 35

6. Draw a shape with a perimeter of 14 units.

What is the area of the shape?

_____ square units

SRB 132 133 136–138

Array Multiplication 1

1. How many squares are in a 4-by-28 array? Make a picture of the array.

Total squares: _____

4 × 28 = _____

2. How many squares are in a 3-by-26 array? Make a picture of the array.

Total squares: _____

3 × 26 = _____

3. How many squares are in a 6-by-32 array? Make a picture of the array.

Total squares: _____

6 × 32 = _____

Use with Lesson 9.3.

(two hundred thirteen) **213**

Geoboard Areas

Record your results in this table.

Geoboard Areas		
Area	**Longer Sides**	**Shorter Sides**
12 square units	units	units
12 square units	units	units
6 square units	units	units
6 square units	units	unit
16 square units	units	units
16 square units	units	units

1. Study your table. Can you find a pattern? _____

_____

_____

_____

2. Find the lengths of the sides of a rectangle or
square whose area is 30 square units without
using the geoboard or geoboard dot paper.
Make or draw the shape to check your answer. _____

3. Make check marks in your table next to the
rectangles and squares whose *perimeters* are
14 units and 16 units.

1. Circle the fractions greater than $\frac{3}{4}$.
Put a star next to the fractions
equivalent to $\frac{3}{4}$.

$\frac{3}{6}$ $\frac{1}{2}$

$\frac{9}{12}$ $\frac{7}{8}$

$\frac{12}{16}$ $\frac{99}{100}$

SRB 27–30

2. Draw a set of 12 circles.

Color $\frac{5}{12}$ of the set blue.

Color $\frac{1}{3}$ of the set red.

Color $\frac{1}{6}$ of the set green.

SRB 24

3. How many sixths are shaded?

_____ sixths

Write the fraction: _____

Write the mixed number: / ___

4. Put in the parentheses needed to
complete the number models.

$2 \times 90 + 7 = 187$

$11 - 4 \times 80 = 560$

$4{,}499 = 50 \times 90 - 1$

SRB 16 17

5. Multiply.

$\begin{array}{r} 58 \\ \times\ 4 \\ \hline \end{array}$ $\begin{array}{r} 37 \\ \times\ 8 \\ \hline \end{array}$ $\begin{array}{r} 49 \\ \times\ 6 \\ \hline \end{array}$

SRB 58–62

6. Measure this line segment.

_____

It is about _____ inches long.

It is about _____ centimeters long.

SRB 119–121 125–127

Using the Partial-Products Algorithm

Multiply. Compare your answers with your partner's answers.
Use a calculator if you disagree.
If you made a mistake on a problem, work it again.

Example 7 × 46 $$\begin{array}{r} 46 \\ \times\ 7 \\ \hline \end{array}$$ 7 [40s]→ 280 7 [6s]→ + 42 280 + 42→ 322	**1.** $$\begin{array}{r} 34 \\ \times\ 2 \\ \hline \end{array}$$
2. $$\begin{array}{r} 83 \\ \times\ 5 \\ \hline \end{array}$$	**3.** $$\begin{array}{r} 55 \\ \times\ 6 \\ \hline \end{array}$$
4. $$\begin{array}{r} 214 \\ \times\ \ 7 \\ \hline \end{array}$$	**5.** $$\begin{array}{r} 403 \\ \times\ \ 5 \\ \hline \end{array}$$

Who Am I?

In each riddle, I am a different whole number.
Use the clues to find out who I am.

1. **Clue 1:** I am greater than 30 and less than 40.
   Clue 2: The sum of my digits is less than 5.

   Who am I? _____

2. **Clue 1:** I am greater than 15 and less than 40.
   Clue 2: If you double me, I become a number that ends in 0.
   Clue 3: $\frac{1}{5}$ of me is equal to 5.

   Who am I? _____

3. **Clue 1:** I am less than 100.
   Clue 2: The sum of my digits is 4.
   Clue 3: Half of me is an odd number.

   Who am I? _____

4. **Clue 1:** If you multiply me by 2, I become a number greater than 20 and less than 40.
   Clue 2: If you multiply me by 6, I end in 8.
   Clue 3: If you multiply me by 4, I end in 2.

   Who am I? _____

Challenge

5. **Clue 1:** Double my tens digit to get my ones digit.
   Clue 2: Double me and I am less than 50.

   Who am I? _____

6. **Clue 1:** Double me, and I am greater than 80 and less than 100.
   Clue 2: If you double me, I end in 4.
   Clue 3: My ones digit is greater than my tens digit.

   Who am I? _____

Math Boxes 9.4

1. There are _____ books in $\frac{2}{5}$ of a set of 25 books.

There are _____ minutes in $\frac{3}{4}$ of an hour.

I have 6 books. This is $\frac{1}{6}$ of a set of books. How many books are in the complete set?

_____ books

2. Think:

How many...

$63 \div 7 =$ _____ 7s in 63?

$630 \div 7 =$ _____ 7s in 630?

$48 \div 6 =$ _____ 6s in 48?

$480 \div 6 =$ _____ 6s in 480?

SRB
46 47

3. The length of the longer

side is _____ units.

The length of the shorter

side is _____ units.

The area of the rectangle

is _____ square units.

SRB
138

4. Complete the "What's My Rule?" table.

in

Rule

Add 25 minutes

out

in	out
7:00	
3:15	
5:45	
	7:40
	11:10

SRB
179 180

5. Suppose you like pizza and are very hungry. Would you rather have $\frac{4}{5}$ of a pizza or $\frac{8}{10}$ of a pizza?

_____

Why? _____

_____

_____

SRB
27 28

6. Draw an angle that measures between 180° and 270°.

SRB
149 150

Shopping at the Stock-Up Sale

Use the Stock-Up Sale Poster #2 on page 241 in the *Student Reference Book.* Solve each number story below. Show how you got the answers.

1. When Mason sees bars of soap at the Stock-Up
    Sale, he wants to buy at least 5. He has $4.00.
    If there is no tax, can he buy 5 bars of soap? _____

    Number model: _____

    Can he buy 6 bars? _____

2. Vic's mom gave him a $5.00 bill to buy a toothbrush.
    If he goes to the sale, can he buy 5 toothbrushes? _____

    Suppose there is no tax. Exactly how much
    money does Vic need in order to be able to
    buy 5 toothbrushes at the sale price? _____

    Number model: _____

3. Andrea wants 2 audio tapes. How much more
    will it cost her to buy 5 tapes at the sale price
    rather than 2 tapes at the regular price? _____

4. If the store charges 10 percent sales tax,
    what will the total cost of the 5 audio tapes be? _____

    Number model: _____

5. Make up a Stock-Up Sale story of your own.

    _____

    _____

    _____

    Answer: _____

    Number model: _____

Using the Partial-Products Algorithm

Multiply. Compare your answers with your partner's answers.
Use a calculator if you disagree.
If you did a problem wrong, work it again.

1.   68
      × 2
	2. 96
	      × 5

3.   47
      × 4
	4. 85
	      × 9

5.   231
      × 6
	6. 508
	      × 5

1. Estimate the cost of these items:

4 giant stickers at $0.88 each

about $_____._____

2 packs of file cards at $1.69 each

about $_____._____

 SRB 167

2. Fill in the unit box. Solve.

 Unit

$49 \div 7 =$ _____

$36 \div 9 =$ _____

$54 \div 6 =$ _____

_____ $= 40 \div 8$

_____ $\div 8 = 8$

SRB 46 47

3. What 3-D shape is this a picture of?

O sphere

O cylinder

O pyramid

What is the shape of the base?

_____

SRB 100 101 107

4. Solve.

```
  678          704
+ 492        - 358
```

SRB 51–57

5. Use the partial-products algorithm to solve.

```
  49        652        408
×  7        ×  3        ×  8
```

SRB 58 59

6. Fill in the empty frames and the rule box.

+ 40

| | 83 | | 98 |

| | 73 |

SRB 176 177

Factor Bingo Game Mat

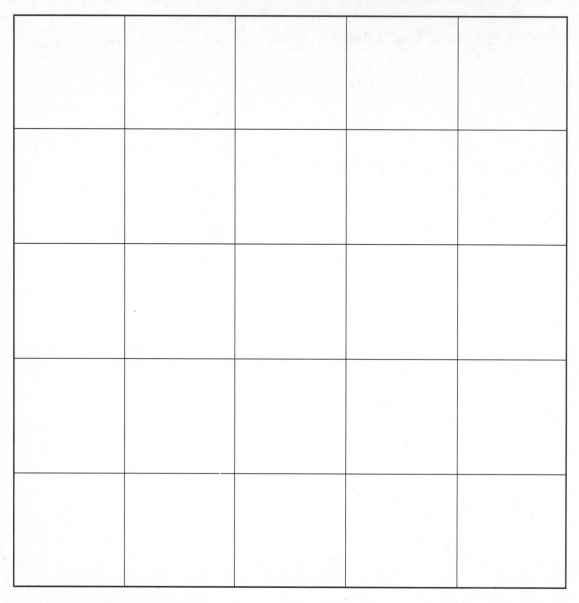

Write any of the numbers
2–90 onto the grid above.

You may use a number
only once.

To help you keep track
of the numbers you use,
circle them in the list.

	2	3	4	5	6	7	8	9	10
11	12	13	14	15	16	17	18	19	20
21	22	23	24	25	26	27	28	29	30
31	32	33	34	35	36	37	38	39	40
41	42	43	44	45	46	47	48	49	50
51	52	53	54	55	56	57	58	59	60
61	62	63	64	65	66	67	68	69	70
71	72	73	74	75	76	77	78	79	80
81	82	83	84	85	86	87	88	89	90

Use with Lesson 9.6.

Using the Partial-Products Algorithm

Multiply. Compare your answers with your partner's answers.
Use a calculator if you disagree.
If you did a problem wrong, work it again.

1.   29
      × 4
	2. 85
	      × 5

3.   93
      × 4
	4. 52
	      × 9

5.   409
      × 5
	6. 432
	      × 8

Math Boxes 9.6

---

1. There are _____ flowers in $\frac{3}{10}$ of a bunch of 10 flowers.

There are _____ minutes in $\frac{1}{4}$ of an hour.

I have 5 cars. This is $\frac{1}{3}$ of a set of cars. How many cars are in the complete set?

_____ cars

2. How many 4s in 2,000? _____

$2,000 \div 4 =$ _____

_____ $\times 4 = 2,000$

What number times 7 = 6,300? _____

$6,300 \div 7 =$ _____

_____ $\times 7 = 6,300$

---

3. The length of the longer

side is _____ units.

The length of the shorter

side is _____ units.

The area of the rectangle

is _____ square units.

SRB
138

4. Determine the total cost.

4 boxes of cereal at $2.98 each $_____

2 gallons of milk at $3.09 each $_____

Total: $_____

SRB
188 189
191 192

---

5. Use the partial-products algorithm to solve.

$$\begin{array}{r} 59 \\ \times\ 3 \\ \hline \end{array} \qquad \begin{array}{r} 489 \\ \times\ 7 \\ \hline \end{array} \qquad \begin{array}{r} 608 \\ \times\ 9 \\ \hline \end{array}$$

SRB
58 59

6. Solve.

$(40 \times 3) \div 2 =$ _____

$4 \times (300 \div 6) =$ _____

$(7 \times 80) + 140 =$ _____

SRB
16 17

Use with Lesson 9.6.

Sharing Money

Work with a partner. Put your play money in a bank for both of you to use.

1. If $54 is shared equally by 3 people, how much does each person get?

   a. How many $10 bills does each person get? _____ $10 bill(s)

   b. How many dollars are left to share? $_____

   c. How many $1 bills does each person get? _____ $1 bill(s)

   d. Number model: $54 ÷ 3 = $_____

2. If $204 is shared equally by 6 people, how much does each person get?

   a. How many $100 bills does each person get? _____ $100 bill(s)

   b. How many $10 bills does each person get? _____ $10 bill(s)

   c. How many dollars are left to share? $_____

   d. How many $1 bills does each person get? _____ $1 bill(s)

   e. Number model: $204 ÷ 6 = $_____

3. If $71 is shared equally by 5 people, how much does each person get?

   a. How many $10 bills does each person get? _____ $10 bill(s)

   b. How many dollars are left to share? $_____

   c. How many $1 bills does each person get? _____ $1 bill(s)

   d. How many $1 bills are left over? _____ $1 bill(s)

   e. If the leftover $1 bills are shared equally,
      how many cents does each person get? _____ ¢

   f. Number model: $71 ÷ 5 = $_____

4. $84 ÷ 3 = $_____

5. $75 ÷ 6 = $_____

6. $181 ÷ 4 = $_____

7. $617 ÷ 5 = $_____

Math Boxes 9.7

---

1. How many fifths are shaded?

___ fifths

Write the fraction: ___

Write the mixed number: ⁄___

---

2. Write 3 fractions that are equivalent to $\frac{8}{12}$.

___   ___   ___

SRB 30

---

3. Write six factors of 12.

___   ___   ___

___   ___   ___

SRB 37

---

4. What part of this pizza has been eaten?

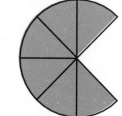

_____

What part is left?

_____

SRB 22 23

---

5. Use the partial-products algorithm to solve.

$$\begin{array}{r} 296 \\ \times\ \ 4 \end{array} \qquad \begin{array}{r} 451 \\ \times\ \ 5 \end{array} \qquad \begin{array}{r} 183 \\ \times\ \ 7 \end{array}$$

SRB 58 59

---

6. Measure this line segment.

It is about _____ inches long.

It is about _____ centimeters long.

SRB 119-121 125-127

Division with Remainders

Solve the problems below. Remember that you will have to decide
what the remainder means in order to answer the questions.
You may use your calculator, counters, or pictures.

1. Ruth is buying soda for a party. There are
   6 cans in a pack. She needs 44 cans.
   How many 6-packs will she buy? _____ 6-packs

2. Paul is buying tickets to the circus.
   Each ticket costs $7. He has $47.
   How many tickets can he buy? _____ tickets

3. Héctor is standing in line for the roller coaster.
   There are 33 people in line.
   Each roller coaster car holds 4 people.
   How many cars are needed to hold 33 people? _____ cars

Pretend that the division key on your calculator is broken.
Solve the following problems:

4. Regina is building a fence around her dollhouse.
   She is making each fence post 5 inches tall.   5 in.
   The wood she bought is 36 inches long.
   How many fence posts does each piece of wood make? _____ posts

   Explain how you found your answer.

   _____

   _____

5. Missy, Ann, and Herman found a $10 bill.
   They want to share the money equally.
   How much money will each person get? _____

   Explain how you found your answer.

   _____

   _____

Using the Partial-Products Algorithm

Multiply. Compare your answers with your partner's answers.
Use a calculator if you disagree.
If you did a problem wrong, work it again.

1. $\begin{array}{r} 43 \\ \times\ 6 \\ \hline \end{array}$	**2.** $\begin{array}{r} 53 \\ \times\ 4 \\ \hline \end{array}$
3. $\begin{array}{r} 68 \\ \times\ 5 \\ \hline \end{array}$	**4.** $\begin{array}{r} 74 \\ \times\ 7 \\ \hline \end{array}$
5. $\begin{array}{r} 167 \\ \times\ 4 \\ \hline \end{array}$	**6.** $\begin{array}{r} 403 \\ \times\ 3 \\ \hline \end{array}$

Use with Lesson 9.8.

Math Boxes 9.8

1. Write the fractions in order from smallest to largest.

$$\frac{1}{3}, \frac{1}{10}, 1\frac{1}{4}, \frac{3}{4}$$

_____ _____ _____ _____

SRB 31 32

2. Determine the total cost.

5 cans of fruit at
$1.19 each $_____._____

3 gallons of ice cream
at $3.85 each $_____._____

Total: $_____._____

SRB 188 189 191 192

3. Toni frosted $\frac{4}{5}$ of the cupcakes. What fraction of the cupcakes are *not* frosted? _____

Did she frost more or less than $\frac{1}{2}$ of the cupcakes? _____

If there were 20 cupcakes in all, how many did she frost?

_____

SRB 22 23 31 32

4. Use bills and coins.

Share $78 equally among 3 people.

Each person gets $_____._____

Share $53 equally among 4 people.

Each person gets $_____._____

SRB 67

5. The length of the longer

side is _____ units.

The length of the shorter

side is _____ units.

The area of the rectangle

is _____ square units.

SRB 138

6. Circle the angle that measures about 90 degrees.

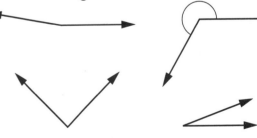

An angle that measures 90° is

called a _____ angle.

SRB 90 149 150

Lattice Multiplication

Megan has a special way of doing multiplication problems. She calls it lattice multiplication. Can you figure out how she does it?

Study the problems and solutions in Column A. Then try to use lattice multiplication to solve the problems in Column B.

Column A	**Column B**

$3 \times 64 = \underline{192}$

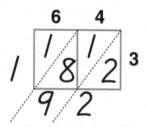

1. $4 \times 65 = \underline{\hspace{2cm}}$

$5 \times 713 = \underline{3,565}$

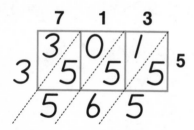

2. $6 \times 815 = \underline{\hspace{2cm}}$

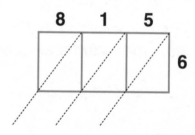

$7 \times 376 = \underline{2,632}$

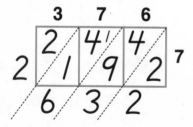

3. $9 \times 634 = \underline{\hspace{2cm}}$

Lattice Multiplication Practice

1. 8 × 45 = _____

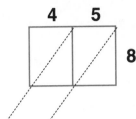

2. 9 × 37 = _____

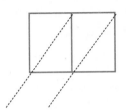

3. 5 × 23 = _____

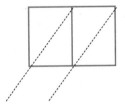

4. 3 × 124 = _____

5. 6 × 431 = _____

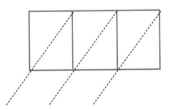

6. 7 × 209 = _____

Fractions of a Sandwich

Alicia's family is planning a family reunion. There are 20 children and 9 adults. Alicia will order extra-long submarine sandwiches for the reunion. Each sandwich is cut into 6 sections.

1. What is the largest number of family members who might come to the reunion? _____ people

2. Suppose that each person eats 1 section of a sandwich.

    a. How many sections of a sandwich are needed? _____ sections

    b. How many sandwiches will Alicia need to buy? _____ sandwiches

    c. How many sections of a sandwich is that? _____ sections

    d. What fraction of a whole sandwich will

        each person eat? _____ of a sandwich

    e. How many whole sandwiches will be eaten? _____ sandwiches

    f. What fraction of a sandwich will be left over? _____ of a sandwich

3. Suppose that each person eats 2 sections of a sandwich.

    a. How many sections of a sandwich are needed? _____ sections

    b. How many sandwiches will Alicia need to buy? _____ sandwiches

    c. How many sections of a sandwich is that? _____ sections

    d. What fraction of a whole sandwich

        will each person eat? _____ of a sandwich

    e. How many whole sandwiches will be eaten? _____ sandwiches

    f. What fraction of a sandwich will be left over? _____ of a sandwich

Use with Lesson 9.9.

1. Fill in the oval next to the best estimate.

$1{,}943 - 488 = $ _____

○ about 1,000

○ about 1,200

○ about 1,500

○ about 1,800

2. How many 4s in 40? _____

How many 4s in 400? _____

How many 4s in 4,000? _____

How many 10s in 400? _____

How many 100s in 40,000? _____

3. Write six factors of 20.

_____   _____   _____

_____   _____   _____

4. Allison has 58 stickers. She wants to share them among 8 friends.

How many stickers does each friend get?

_____

How many stickers are left over?

_____

5. Use the partial-products algorithm to solve.

$$\begin{array}{r} 238 \\ \times\ 6 \\ \hline \end{array} \qquad \begin{array}{r} 574 \\ \times\ 5 \\ \hline \end{array} \qquad \begin{array}{r} 706 \\ \times\ 7 \\ \hline \end{array}$$

6. Put in the parentheses needed to complete the number models.

$15 + 80 \times 90 = 7{,}215$

$14 - 6 \times 800 = 6{,}400$

$60 \times 79 + 1 = 4{,}800$

Array Multiplication 2

1. How many squares are in a 20-by-13 array?

Total squares = _____

20 × 13 = _____

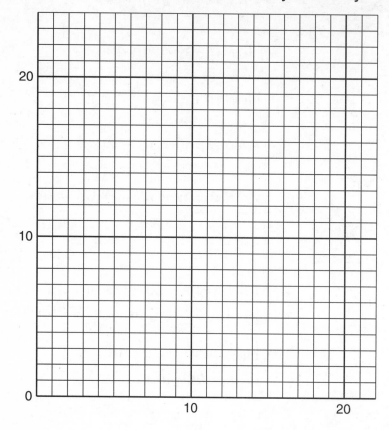

2. How many squares are in an 18-by-30 array?

Total squares = _____

18 × 30 = _____

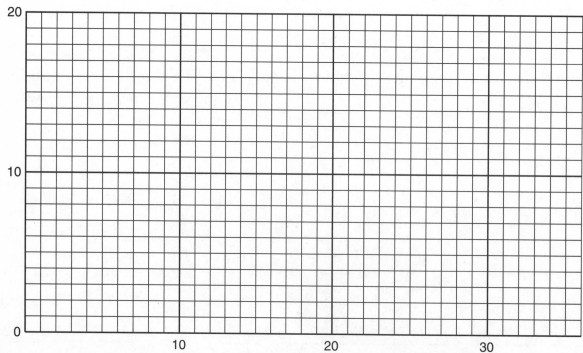

Use with Lessons 9.10 and 9.11.

Array Multiplication 3

1. How many squares are in a 17-by-34 array?   Total squares = _____

                                               17×34 = _____

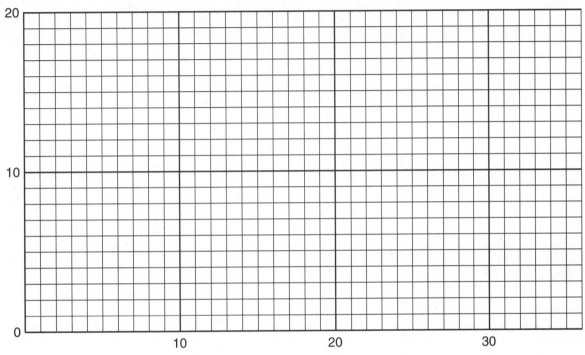

2. How many squares are in a 22-by-28 array?   Total squares = _____

                                               22×28 = _____

Math Boxes 9.10

1. Fill in the missing numbers on the number line.

2. Find the total cost.

3 boxes of fruit bars
at $1.89 each $_____

2 quarts of juice
at $1.75 each $_____

Total: $_____

SRB
188 189
191 192

3. Find the area of the rectangle.

60 cm

20 cm

_____ × _____ = _____ cm²
length of   length of   area
short side   long side

SRB
138

4. Use bills and coins.

Share $108 equally among
4 people.

Each gets $_____

Share $61 equally among
4 people.

Each gets $_____

SRB
67

5. Practice lattice multiplication.

493
× 6

4   9   3

6

SRB
60–62

6. Cross out the names that do not belong.

$\frac{2}{5}$

$\frac{4}{10}$ $\frac{20}{50}$ $\frac{2}{6}$

$\frac{6}{15}$ $\frac{8}{20}$ $1\frac{1}{5}$

SRB
14   15
30

Multiplication with Multiples of 10

Multiply. Compare your answers with your partner's answer.
Use a calculator if you disagree.
If you did a problem wrong, work it again.

| **Example** | 30 |
| | × 26 |

$$20[30s] \rightarrow \quad 600$$
$$6[30s] \rightarrow +180$$
$$\overline{780}$$

1.
$$\begin{array}{r} 70 \\ \times\ 18 \\ \hline \end{array}$$

2.
$$\begin{array}{r} 88 \\ \times\ 40 \\ \hline \end{array}$$

3.
$$\begin{array}{r} 60 \\ \times\ 35 \\ \hline \end{array}$$

4.
$$\begin{array}{r} 80 \\ \times\ 44 \\ \hline \end{array}$$

5.
$$\begin{array}{r} 90 \\ \times\ 63 \\ \hline \end{array}$$

Math Boxes 9.11

1. Write the fractions in order from smallest to largest.

$\frac{5}{6}, \frac{4}{12}, \frac{2}{3}, \frac{1}{100}$

____ ____ ____ ____

SRB
31 32

2. Solve. Use your calculator. Pretend the division key is broken.

$152 \div 8 =$ _____
Think: How many 8s in 152?

$285 \div 3 =$ _____
Think: How many 3s in 285?

3. Name eight factors of 24.

____ ____ ____ ____

____ ____ ____ ____

SRB
37

4. Practice lattice multiplication.

$$\begin{array}{r} 324 \\ \times \quad 6 \end{array}$$

3   **2**   **4**

6

SRB
60–62

5. Fill in the unit box. Solve.

Unit

$6 \times 6 =$ _____

$7 \times 9 =$ _____

_____ $= 8 \times 5$

_____ $= 9 \times 9$

_____ $= 9 \times 6$

SRB
46 47

6.

6 yd
15 yd

This shape is a

_____.

The perimeter is _____ yards.

SRB
98 99
132 133

238 (two hundred thirty-eight)

2-Digit Multiplication

Multiply using the partial-products algorithm. Compare your answers with
your partner's answers. Use a calculator if you disagree.
If you did a problem wrong, work it again.

1. $\begin{array}{r} 24 \\ \times\ 16 \\ \hline \end{array}$	**2.** $\begin{array}{r} 42 \\ \times\ 31 \\ \hline \end{array}$	**3.** $\begin{array}{r} 12 \\ \times\ 87 \\ \hline \end{array}$
4. $\begin{array}{r} 59 \\ \times\ 79 \\ \hline \end{array}$	**5.** $\begin{array}{r} 36 \\ \times\ 14 \\ \hline \end{array}$	**6.** $\begin{array}{r} 42 \\ \times\ 53 \\ \hline \end{array}$
7. $\begin{array}{r} 23 \\ \times\ 81 \\ \hline \end{array}$	**8.** $\begin{array}{r} 63 \\ \times\ 12 \\ \hline \end{array}$	**9.** $\begin{array}{r} 49 \\ \times\ 38 \\ \hline \end{array}$

Accurate Measures

Use fractions to carefully measure these drawings using both the inch and centimeter sides of your ruler.

1.

The length of the fish

about _____ in.   about _____ cm

2.   Alpha   Beta

The map distance from Alpha to Beta

about _____ in.   about _____ cm

3.

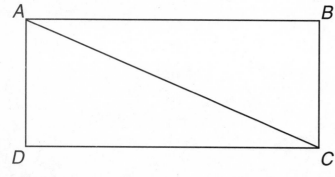

Line segment *AB*: about _____ in.

Line segment *AB*: about _____ cm

Line segment *AC*: about _____ in.

Line segment *AC*: about _____ cm

Carefully draw the following line segments:

4. 9.5 cm

5. $4\frac{1}{4}$ in.

6. 2 cm shorter than 9.5 cm

7. $1\frac{1}{4}$ in. shorter than $4\frac{1}{4}$ in.

Math Boxes 9.12

1.

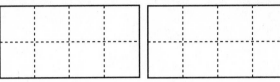

Shade $1\frac{3}{8}$.

How many eighths are shaded?

_____ eighths

Write the fraction: _____

Write the mixed number: $/$ _____

2. How many 10s are in each number?

400   _____ tens

150   _____ tens

1,600   _____ tens

2,430   _____ tens

3. Use the partial-products algorithm to solve.

$$\begin{array}{r} 92 \\ \times\ 60 \\ \hline \end{array} \qquad \begin{array}{r} 37 \\ \times\ 50 \\ \hline \end{array}$$

4. Make an estimate. About how much money, without tax, will you need for 5 cans of juice that cost $2.89 each?

about _____

5. Practice lattice multiplication.

$43 \times 68 =$ _____

6. Use bills and coins.

Share $45.90 equally among 3 people.

Each gets $_____

Share $49.20 equally among 4 people.

Each gets $_____

Number Stories with Positive and Negative Numbers

Solve the following problems.

1. Jim records his weight change weekly.
   This week he recorded −3 pounds.

   Can you tell how much he weighs? _____

2. The largest change in temperature in a single day took
   place in January 1916 in Browning, Montana. The
   temperature dropped 100°F that day. The temperature
   was 44°F when it started dropping.

   How low did it go? _____

3. The largest temperature rise in 12 hours took place in Granville,
   North Dakota, on February 21, 1918. The temperature rose
   83°F that day. The high temperature was 50°F.

   What was the low temperature? _____

4. On January 12, 1911, the temperature in Rapid City,
   South Dakota, fell from 49°F at 6 A.M. to −13°F at 8 A.M.

   By how many degrees did the
   temperature drop in those 2 hours? _____

5. The highest temperature ever recorded in Verkhoyansk,
   Siberia, was 98°F. The lowest temperature ever recorded
   there was −94°F.

   What is the difference between those
   two temperatures? _____

6. Write your own number story using positive and negative
   numbers.

   _____

   _____

   _____

°F
220
210
200
190
180
170
160
150
140
130
120
110
100
90
80
70
60
50
40
30
20
10
0
−10
−20
−30
−40

Multiplication Strategies

Try using your favorite strategy to solve each problem. Compare your answers with your partner's answers. Use a calculator if you disagree. If you make a mistake, solve the problem again.

1. $\begin{array}{r} 96 \\ \times\ \ 8 \\ \hline \end{array}$	**2.** $\begin{array}{r} 362 \\ \times\ \ \ 7 \\ \hline \end{array}$
3. $\begin{array}{r} 70 \\ \times\ 45 \\ \hline \end{array}$	**4.** $\begin{array}{r} 90 \\ \times\ 83 \\ \hline \end{array}$
5. $\begin{array}{r} 87 \\ \times\ 56 \\ \hline \end{array}$	**6.** $\begin{array}{r} 63 \\ \times\ 44 \\ \hline \end{array}$

7. My favorite multiplication strategy is _____ .

I like this strategy best because _____

_____

1. There are 24 children in
Mrs. Little's class.

$\frac{1}{2}$ of the children play soccer.
How many children play soccer?

_____ children

$\frac{1}{3}$ of the children play a musical
instrument. How many children
play a musical instrument?

_____ children

2. Find the area of the rectangle.

80 in.

40 in.

_____ $\times$ _____ = _____ in.^{2}
length of   length of   area
short side   long side

3. Name eight factors of 36.

____ ____ ____ ____

____ ____ ____ ____

4. Solve. Use your calculator.
Pretend the division key is broken.

$144 \div 9 =$ _____
Think: How many 9s in 144?

$465 \div 3 =$ _____
Think: How many 3s in 465?

5. Use the partial-products algorithm
to solve.

$$\begin{array}{r} 35 \\ \times\ 62 \end{array} \qquad \begin{array}{r} 49 \\ \times\ 31 \end{array}$$

6. Practice lattice multiplication.

$74 \times 28 =$ _____

Math Boxes 9.14

1. Measure this line segment.

_____

It is about _____ inches long.

Draw a line segment $1\frac{3}{4}$ inches long.

SRB
125–127

2. Measure this line segment.

_____

It is about _____ centimeters long.

Draw a line segment
3.5 centimeters long.

SRB
119–121

3. Circle the most appropriate unit.

length of calculator:

    inches   feet   miles

weight of an adult:

    ounces   pounds   tons

amount of gas in car:

    cups   pints   gallons

4. Solve.

1 foot = _____ inches

_____ feet = 36 inches

1 yard = _____ feet

_____ yards = 15 feet

1 yard = _____ inches

SRB
128 129

5. Find the median of the following numbers.

34, 56, 34, 16, 33, 27, 45

Median: _____

SRB
74

6. Circle the tool you would use to find

length of a pen:

    ruler   compass   scale

weight of a dime:

    ruler   compass   scale

way to get home:

    ruler   compass   scale

SRB
144–146

Review: Units of Measure

1. Measure in centimeters. Which is longer, the path from *A* to *B* or the path from *C* to *D*? _____

How much longer is it? _____

2. On the top edge of the ruler, make a dot at $3\frac{1}{2}$ inches. Label it *E*.

3. Make a dot at $4\frac{3}{4}$ in. Label it *F*.

4. Make a dot at $2\frac{7}{8}$ in. Label it *G*.

5. What is the distance from *E* to *F*? _____ in.

6. From *E* to *G*? _____ in.

7. From *F* to *G*? _____ in.

Complete.

8. 3 yd = _____ ft

9. 4 yd 1 ft = _____ ft

10. 1 ft 8 in. = _____ in.

11. 7 ft = _____ yd _____ ft

Measure the sides of the rectangle in centimeters. Find the area.

12. Area: _____
(unit)

Challenge

Measure the sides of the rectangle in centimeters. Find the area.

13. Area: _____
(unit)

Use with Lesson 10.1.

Earth Layers

Earth is made of layers. The outer layer (the part you stand on) is called the crust. Compared to the other layers, the crust is very thin—it ranges from 8 to 80 kilometers in depth. If Earth were a huge egg, the crust would not be much thicker than the shell.

The picture is a scale drawing of Earth's layers. In the drawing, each centimeter stands for 1,000 kilometers. You can estimate the actual thickness of each layer by measuring with a centimeter ruler. For example, the lower mantle in the drawing is about 2.1 centimeters wide. This tells you that the actual thickness is about 2,100 kilometers.

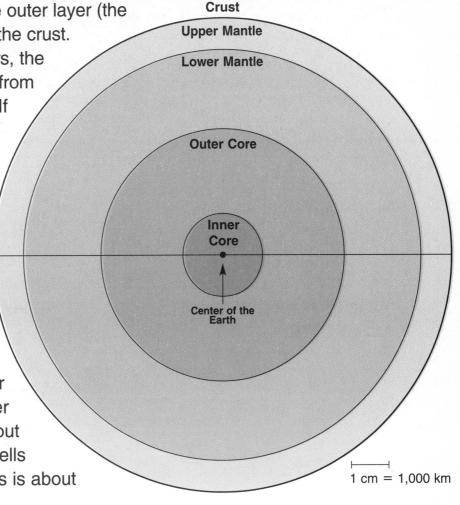

Crust
Upper Mantle
Lower Mantle
Outer Core
Inner Core
Center of the Earth

1 cm = 1,000 km

1. Imagine that you could dig a hole to the center of Earth. About how deep would the hole be?   about _____ kilometers

2. What is the diameter of Earth?   about _____ kilometers

3. The closer you get to the center of Earth, the hotter it gets. Study the data in the table. In which layer is the temperature about 800°C?

_____

4. In which layer is the temperature about 3,000°C?

Temperatures Inside Earth	
50 km below the surface	about 800°C
1,000 km below the surface	about 1,800°C
2,000 km below the surface	about 3,000°C
3,200 km below the surface	about 3,500°C
at the center of Earth	about 4,000°C

_____

Math Boxes 10.1

---

1. What temperature is 30° warmer than −20°C?

_____ °C

How much colder is −5°F than 10°F?

_____ ° colder

SRB
154

---

2. Use the partial-products algorithm to solve.

$$\begin{array}{r} 86 \\ \times\ 27 \\ \hline \end{array} \qquad \begin{array}{r} 91 \\ \times\ 64 \\ \hline \end{array}$$

SRB
58   59

---

3. Write six numbers that are factors of 18.

_____   _____   _____

_____   _____   _____

SRB
37

---

4. A hexagon is ONE. Shade $1\frac{2}{3}$.

What fraction is not shaded?

_____

---

5. Make an estimate. About how much money, without tax, will you need for 5 gallons of milk that cost $3.09 each?

about _____

SRB
167

---

6. Solve.

$(7 \times 7) + 11 =$ _____

$100 - (8 \times 9) =$ _____

_____ $= (4 \times 9) + (6 \times 8)$

SRB
16   17

---

248 (two hundred forty-eight)

Volume of Boxes

Part 1   Use the patterns on *Math Masters,* page 166 to
build Boxes A, B, C, and D. Record the results
in the table.

height

base

Box	Number of cm Cubes		Area of Base	Height	Volume
	Estimate	Exact	(square cm)	(cm)	(cubic cm)
A					
B					
C					
D					

Part 2   The following patterns are for Boxes E, F, and G. Each square
stands for 1 square centimeter. Find the volume of each box.
(Do not cut out the patterns.)

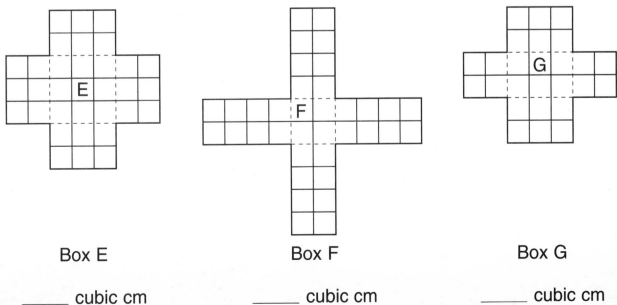

Box E

Box F

Box G

_____ cubic cm

_____ cubic cm

_____ cubic cm

Multiplication Practice

Use your favorite multiplication algorithm to solve the following problems.
Then, compare answers with your partner. Use a calculator if you disagree.
If you made a mistake on a problem, try to solve it again.

1. $\begin{array}{r} 427 \\ \times\ \ \ 3 \\ \hline \end{array}$	**2.** $\begin{array}{r} 505 \\ \times\ \ \ 8 \\ \hline \end{array}$
3. $\begin{array}{r} 20 \\ \times\ 90 \\ \hline \end{array}$	**4.** $\begin{array}{r} 67 \\ \times\ 40 \\ \hline \end{array}$
5. $\begin{array}{r} 74 \\ \times\ 35 \\ \hline \end{array}$	**6.** $\begin{array}{r} 37 \\ \times\ 58 \\ \hline \end{array}$

Weight and Volume

Complete Parts 1 and 2 before the start of Lesson 10.5.

Part 1 Try to order the objects on display from heaviest to lightest. Lift them to help you guess. Record your guesses below.

Names of objects in order

heaviest _____

2nd heaviest _____

3rd heaviest _____

lightest _____

Part 2 Try to order the objects on display from largest to smallest volume. Record your guesses below.

Names of objects in order

largest _____

2nd largest _____

3rd largest _____

smallest _____

Complete Parts 3 and 4 as part of Lesson 10.5.

Part 3 Record the actual order of the objects from heaviest to lightest. Were your guesses correct?

Names of objects in order

heaviest _____

2nd heaviest _____

3rd heaviest _____

lightest _____

Part 4 Record the actual order of the objects from largest to smallest volume. Were your guesses correct?

Names of objects in order

largest _____

2nd largest _____

3rd largest _____

smallest _____

Review Complete the number models

1. $(3 \times 8) - 7 =$ _____

   $3 \times (8 - 7) =$ _____

2. _____ $= (18 \div 2) + 4$

   _____ $= 18 \div (2 + 4)$

3. $(15 + 25) - 8 =$ _____

   $15 + (25 - 8) =$ _____

4. _____ $= (6 + 4) \times (6 - 4)$

   _____ $= 6 + (4 \times 6) - 4$

5. $37 - (12 - 5) =$ _____

   $(37 - 12) - 5 =$ _____

6. _____ $= (24 \div 4) \div 2$

   _____ $= 24 \div (4 \div 2)$

Math Boxes 10.2

---

1. What is the median number of pets?

_____ pet(s)

Number of Pets	Number of Children
0	///
1	## ##
2	##
3	///
4	/
5	/

2. What is this 3-dimensional shape called?

O rectangular prism

O pyramid

O sphere

How many faces does it have?

_____ faces

---

3. There are 20 crayons in a box.
$\frac{1}{2}$ of the crayons are broken.

How many crayons are broken?

_____ crayons

$\frac{1}{4}$ of the crayons are red.

How many crayons are red?

_____ crayons

4. Measure this line segment.

_____

It is about _____ inches long.

It is about _____ centimeters long.

---

5. Fill in the unit box.
Solve.

Unit

$56 \div 8 =$ _____

_____ $= 63 \div 7$

_____ $= 24 \div 8$

_____ $= 54 \div 9$

$64 \div 8 =$ _____

6. Circle the fractions less than $\frac{2}{3}$.
Put a star next to the fractions equivalent to $\frac{2}{3}$.

$1\frac{2}{3}$ $\frac{1}{3}$

$\frac{4}{6}$ $\frac{2}{5}$

$\frac{6}{9}$ $\frac{5}{6}$

Body Measures

Work with a partner to make each measurement to the nearest $\frac{1}{4}$ inch.

	Adult at Home	**Me (Now)**	**Me (Later)**
Date			
height	about _____ in.	about _____ in.	about _____ in.
shoe length	about _____ in.	about _____ in.	about _____ in.
around neck	about _____ in.	about _____ in.	about _____ in.
around wrist	about _____ in.	about _____ in.	about _____ in.
waist to floor	about _____ in.	about _____ in.	about _____ in.
forearm	about _____ in.	about _____ in.	about _____ in.
hand span	about _____ in.	about _____ in.	about _____ in.
arm span	about _____ in.	about _____ in.	about _____ in.
_____	about _____ in.	about _____ in.	about _____ in.
_____	about _____ in.	about _____ in.	about _____ in.

←—forearm—→

hand span

←— arm span —→

Math Boxes 10.3

---

1. Find the distance between each pair of numbers.

2 and −6 _____

−7 and 15 _____

100 and −500 _____

2. Practice lattice multiplication.

84 × 56 = _____

---

3. Fill in the missing numbers on the number line.

_____   _____ _____

4. Draw an angle that measures between 180° and 270°.

---

5. Fill in the unit box. Solve.

Unit

_____ × 8 = 32

_____ × 5 = 40

_____ × 6 = 36

81 = 9 × _____

45 = 5 × _____

6. Use bills and coins.

Share $63.75 equally among 3 people.

Each gets $_____

Share $63.00 equally among 5 people.

Each gets $_____

Use with Lesson 10.3.

Scales

Refer to pages 147 and 148 in your *Student Reference Book*. For each scale shown, list three things you could weigh on the scale.

balance scale

_____

_____

_____

market scale

_____

_____

_____

package scale

_____

_____

_____

bath scale

_____

_____

_____

spring scale

_____

_____

_____

produce scale

_____

_____

_____

letter scale

_____

_____

_____

platform scale

_____

_____

_____

infant scale

_____

_____

_____

diet/food scale

_____

_____

_____

Reading Scales

Read each scale and record the weight.

1. _____ g

2. _____ lb

3. _____ lb

4. _____ lb

5. _____ oz

256 (two hundred fifty-six)

Use with Lesson 10.4.

Silly Stories

Refer to the Adult Weights of North American Animals Poster on journal pages 206 and 207 to solve the number stories.

1. If a 30-pound raccoon and a 150-pound deer both stood on a scale, what weight would the scale show?

   _____

2. If five 40-pound beavers climbed on one side of a pan balance, which animal might sit on the other pan so they balance?

   _____

   _____

3. If a 3,000-pound beluga whale, a 6,000-pound pilot whale, a 50,000-pound gray whale, and an 80,000-pound right whale lay on a platform scale (it would have to be huge!), what weight would the scale show? _____

   Which single whale could weigh this much? _____

4. One side of a pan balance has 50 three-pound Gila monsters. The other side of the pan balance has 10 five-pound snowshoe hares. How many of which animal could you add to one of the pans so that the pans balance? _____

   Would the animals go on the pan with the Gila monsters or the snowshoe hares? _____

5. Write and solve a problem of your own.

   _____

   _____

   _____

Math Boxes 10.4

1. Complete the bar graph.

Eli biked 4 miles.

Kate biked 5 miles.

Joe biked 2 miles.

2. Fill in the oval next to the best estimate.

$747 + 932 =$ _____

◯ about 1,500

◯ about 1,700

◯ about 2,000

◯ about 2,500

3. Write six numbers that are factors of 28.

_____ _____ _____

_____ _____ _____

4. Use your Pattern-Block Template to trace three shapes that are regular polygons.

5. Draw two ways to show $\frac{5}{4}$.

6. Draw a line segment $1\frac{3}{4}$ inches long.

Draw a line segment $\frac{1}{2}$ inch longer than the one you just drew.

Use with Lesson 10.4.

Math Boxes 10.5

1. Write the missing numbers.

_____ −30 _____ _____ _____ 10

SRB
39

2. Use the partial-products algorithm to solve.

$$\begin{array}{r} 36 \\ \times\ 25 \\ \hline \end{array} \qquad \begin{array}{r} 43 \\ \times\ 65 \\ \hline \end{array}$$

SRB
58 59

3. Draw a set of 12 Xs. Circle 9 of them.

What fraction of the Xs are circled?

_____

Write an equivalent fraction.

_____

SRB
24 30

4. The degree measure of the angle is:

○ 180°

○ less than 90°

○ less than 270°

○ 290°

SRB
149 150

5. Read the scale and record the weight. _____ lb

SRB
147 148

6. Adam built a rectangular prism out of base-10 blocks. He used 30 cm cubes to make the base. He put 4 more layers of cubes on top of that. What is the volume of the prism he built?

_____ cubic centimeters

SRB
141

Units of Measure

Mark the unit you would use to measure each item.

1. thickness of a dime   O millimeter   O gram   O foot

2. flour used in cooking   O gallon   O cup   O liter

3. gasoline for a car   O fluid ounce   O ton   O gallon

4. distance to the moon   O foot   O square mile   O kilometer

5. area of a floor   O square foot   O cubic foot   O foot

6. package of meat   O yard   O ounce   O ton

7. draperies   O kilometer   O millimeter   O yard

8. diameter of a basketball   O mile   O inch   O square inch

9. perimeter of a garden   O yard   O square yard   O centimeter

10. spices in a recipe   O teaspoon   O pound   O fluid ounce

11. weight of a nickel   O pound   O gram   O inch

12. volume of a suitcase   O square inch   O foot   O cubic inch

13. length of a cat's tail   O centimeter   O meter   O yard

Mark the best answer.

14. How much can an 8-year-old grow in a year?
     O about 2 in.   O about 2 ft   O about 1 yd   O about 1 m

15. How long would it take you to walk 3 miles?
     O about 10 min   O about 20 min   O about 1 hour   O about 5 hours

Challenge

One liter of water weighs 1 kilogram.

16. How many grams does 1 milliliter of water weigh? _____ g

17. How many grams does 0.1 liter of water weigh? _____ g

Metric Weights

1. Two regular-size paper clips weigh about 1 gram.

    a. About how many paper clips would weigh
        10 grams? _____

    b. About how many would weigh 1 kilogram? _____

    c. 0.5 kilogram? _____

2. One ounce is about 30 grams.

    a. About how many regular-size paper clips
        are in 1 ounce? _____

    b. 1 pound? _____

3. About how many grams does a box of
    100 paper clips weigh if the empty box weighs
    about 5 grams? _____

4. A ream of paper has 500 sheets. Most reams
    of copying paper weigh a little more than
    2 kilograms each. About how many grams
    does 1 sheet of paper weigh? _____

Review Solve.

5. $\begin{array}{r} 35 \\ \times\ 4 \\ \hline \end{array}$

6. $\begin{array}{r} 62 \\ \times\ 3 \\ \hline \end{array}$

7. $\begin{array}{r} 285 \\ \times\ 6 \\ \hline \end{array}$

8. Write a number story for one of the problems you just solved.

    _____

    _____

    _____

    _____

Math Boxes 10.6

1. What is the median number of hours children sleep each night?

_____ hours

Hours	Number of Children
8	////
9	//// ////
10	////
11	/

SRB 74

2. Add the parentheses needed to complete the number models.

$$4 \times 5 + 6 \times 9 = 74$$

$$3 \times 16 - 7 = 27$$

$$670 - 240 + 300 = 730$$

SRB 16 17

3. Complete the fraction number story.

Caitlin ate $\dfrac{\square}{8}$ of the pizza.

Madison ate $\dfrac{\square}{8}$ of the pizza.

Kyle ate $\dfrac{\square}{8}$ of the pizza.

$\dfrac{\square}{8}$ of the pizza was left over.

SRB 188 189

4. What is this 3-dimensional shape called?

O rectangular prism

O pyramid

O sphere

How many vertices does it have?

_____ vertices

SRB 103 105

5. Circle the unit you would use to measure each item.

weight of journal   oz   pound   ton

length of car   inch   yard   mile

length of paper clip   cm   meter   kilometer

SRB 119–121 144–146

6. Write at least 5 names for $\dfrac{4}{5}$.

$\dfrac{4}{5}$

SRB 27–30

Use with Lesson 10.6.

A Mean (or Average) Number of Children

Activity 1 Make a bar graph of the data in the table.

Family Sizes	
Family	**Number of Children**
Kugel	5
Abuka	1
Lauer	2
Miller	7
Ellis	1
Bosnak	2

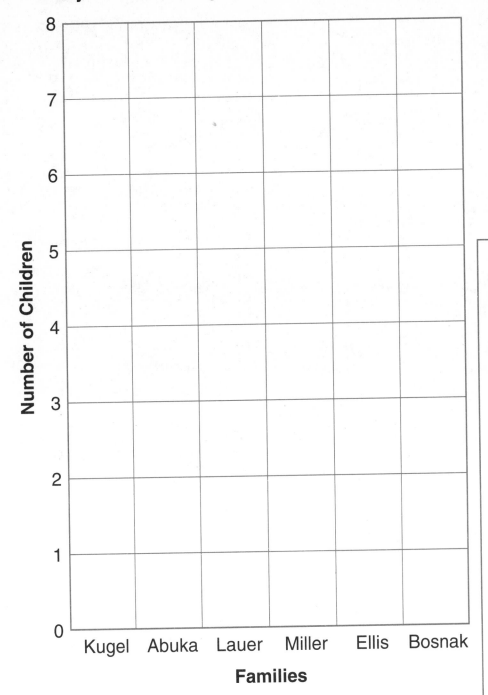

Number of Children (vertical axis)

Kugel Abuka Lauer Miller Ellis Bosnak

Families

The mean, or average, number of children in the six families in the table is _____.

**Activity 2
(to be done later)**

Use the table above. List the number of children in order.

_____

_____

_____

_____

_____

_____

The median number of children in the six families in the table is

_____.

A Mean (or Average) Number of Eggs

Activity 1 Make a bar graph of the data in the table.

Ostrich Clutches	
Clutch	Number of Eggs
a	6
b	10
c	4
d	2
e	8

Number of Eggs

Ostrich Clutches

The mean, or average, number of eggs in the five clutches is _____.

Activity 2 (to be done later)

List the number of eggs in the clutches in order.

_____

_____

_____

_____

_____

The median is _____ eggs per clutch.

Use with Lesson 10.7.

1. Put these numbers in order from smallest to largest.

0   6   −3   0.15

_____ , _____ , _____ , _____

2. Write eight numbers that are factors of 30.

_____ _____ _____ _____

_____ _____ _____ _____

3. Practice lattice multiplication.

39 × 48 = _____

4. How many thirds are shaded?

_____ thirds

Write the fraction: _____

Write the mixed number: _____

5. Read the scale and record the weight.

_____ lb

6. Complete.

1 gallon = _____ quarts

_____ gallons = 12 quarts

1 pint = _____ cups

_____ pints = 14 cups

1 cup = _____ fl oz

_____ cups = 72 fl oz

Finding the Median and the Mean

1. The median (middle) arm span in my class is about _____ inches.

2. The mean (average) arm span in my class is about _____ inches.

3. Look at page 253 in your journal. Use the measurements for an adult and the *second* measurements for yourself to find the median and mean arm spans and heights for your group. Record the results in the table below.

   a. Find the median and mean arm spans of the *adults* for your group.

   b. Find the median and mean arm spans of the *children* for your group.

   c. Find the median and mean heights of the *adults* for your group.

   d. Find the median and mean heights of the *children* for your group.

Summary of Measurements for Your Group

Measure	Adults	Children
Median arm span		
Mean arm span		
Median height		
Mean height		

Find the mean of each set of data.

4. High temperatures: 56°F, 62°F, 74°F, 68°F   Mean: _____ °F

5. Low temperatures: 32°F, 42°F, 58°F, 60°F   Mean: _____ °F

6. Ticket sales: $710, $650, $905   Mean: $ _____

7. Throws: 40 ft, 32 ft, 55 ft, 37 ft, 43 ft, 48 ft   Mean: _____ ft

Use with Lesson 10.8.

Measurement Number Stories

1. The gas tank of Mrs. Rone's car holds about 12 gallons. About how many gallons are in the tank when the gas gauge shows the tank to be $\frac{3}{4}$ full?

    workspace

    _____

2. When the gas tank of Mrs. Rone's car is about half empty, she stops to fill the tank. If gas costs $1.25 per gallon, about how much does it cost to fill the tank?

    _____

Harry's room measures 11 feet by 13 feet. The door to his room is 3 feet wide. He wants to put a wooden border, or baseboard, around the base of the walls.

3. Draw a diagram of Harry's room on the grid below. Show where the door is. Let each side of a grid square equal 1 foot.

4. How many feet of baseboard must Harry buy? _____

5. How many yards is that? _____

6. If baseboard costs $4.00 a yard, how much will Harry pay? _____

workspace

1. The mean, or average, number of books read is _____.

Books Read

Max   Li   Kay   Tim

2. Fill in the unit box. Solve.

Unit

$490 \div 7 =$ _____

$4{,}200 \div 60 =$ _____

$3{,}500 \div 5 =$ _____

_____ $= 2{,}700 \div 90$

3. Fill in the missing numbers on the number line.

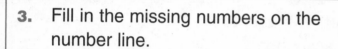

$2 \qquad 2\frac{1}{5}$

_____ _____

4. Explain why this shape is a regular polygon.

_____

_____

_____

_____

_____

5. Grace built a rectangular prism out of base-10 blocks. She used 50 cm cubes to make the base. She put 9 more layers of cubes on top of that. What is the volume of the prism she built?

_____ cubic centimeters

6. Draw a line segment 5.6 centimeters long.

Draw a line segment 1.5 centimeters longer than the one you just drew.

Calculator Memory

For each problem:

- Press the keys on the calculator.
- Guess what number is in memory.
- Record your guess.
- Press (MRC) to check your guess.
- Record the answer.

After each problem, press (MRC) twice and (ON/C) to clear everything.
The display should look like this [0.] before you start a new problem.

Press these keys	Your Guess	Press (MRC) Answer
1. (MRC) (ON/C) (7) (M+) (9) (M+)	_____	_____
2. (2) (0) (M+) (1) (6) (M−)	_____	_____
3. (5) (M+) (1) (0) (M+) (2) (0) (M+)	_____	_____
4. (1) (2) (+) (8) (M+) (6) (M−)	_____	_____
5. (1) (5) (−) (9) (M+) (2) (M−)	_____	_____
6. (2) (5) (M+) (7) (+) (8) (M−)	_____	_____
7. (3) (0) (M+) (1) (5) (−) (5) (M+)	_____	_____
8. (2) (+) (2) (M+) (2) (−) (2) (M+) (2) (+) (2) (M+)	_____	_____

Review Solve.

9. $8 + (2 \times 7) =$ _____

10. $(8 + 2) \times 7 =$ _____

11. $(24 - 9) \times 2 =$ _____

12. $24 - (9 \times 2) =$ _____

13. _____ $= (36 - 22) - 14$

14. _____ $= 36 - (22 - 14)$

15. _____ $= 35 + (20 - 15)$

16. _____ $= (35 + 20) - 15$

17. _____ $= 35 - (20 + 15)$

18. _____ $= (35 - 20) + 15$

Math Boxes 10.9

1. Complete.

Area of Base (square cm)	Height (cm)	Volume (cubic cm)
40	7	
35	6	
100	30	
40	50	

SRB 141

2. Write 5 fractions greater than $\frac{4}{10}$.

____ ____ ____ ____ ____

Write 5 fractions less than $\frac{4}{10}$.

____ ____ ____ ____ ____

Write 3 other names for $\frac{4}{10}$.

____ ____ ____

SRB 31 32

3. Shade $\frac{3}{5}$ of the rectangle.

What fraction is not shaded?

_____

SRB 22 23

4. Draw an angle that measures approximately 90°.

An angle that measures 90° is

called a _____ angle.

SRB 90

5. Name 4 objects that weigh less than 1 pound.

_____

_____

_____

_____

SRB 144 145

6. Complete.

1 quart = _____ pints

_____ quarts = 16 pints

1 quart = _____ fl oz

_____ quarts = 96 fl oz

1 gallon = _____ fl oz

SRB 142 143

Use with Lesson 10.9.

Math Boxes 10.10

---

1. Find the mean (average) for the set of data.

Weekly allowances:

$15, $12, $5, $8

The mean (average) weekly allowance is

$_____.

SRB
77–79

---

2. Fill in the missing numbers on the number line.

$1\frac{7}{8}$ $2\frac{1}{4}$

_____ _____   _____

---

3. There are _____ lollipops in $\frac{1}{5}$ of a box of 25 lollipops.

There are _____ minutes in $\frac{5}{6}$ of an hour.

I have 7 stickers. This is $\frac{1}{7}$ of a set of stickers. How many stickers are in the complete set?

_____ stickers

---

4. Circle the unit you would use to measure each item.

area of desk top	square inch	square yard	cubic meter
volume of fish tank	square mile	cubic inch	gram
capacity of drinking glass	gallon	cup	quart

SRB
136–141

---

5. Solve.

$(9 \times 9) - (43 + 9) = $ _____

_____ $= (5{,}600 \div 80) \div 2$

_____ $= 963 + (567 - 439)$

SRB
16   17

---

6. Complete the bar graph.

Mel caught 5 fish.
Jen caught 4 fish.
Tia caught 1 fish.

SRB
80   81

Frequency Table

1. Fill in the table of waist-to-floor measurements for the class. This kind of table is called a frequency table.

Waist-to-Floor Measurement (inches)	Frequency	
	Tallies	Number
Total =		

2. What is the median (middle value) of the measurements? _____ in.

3. What is the mean (average) of the measurements? _____ in.

4. The *mode* is the measurement, or measurements, that occur most often. What is the mode of the waist-to-floor measurements for the class? _____ in.

Bar Graph

Make a bar graph of the data in the frequency table on journal page 272.

Waist-to-Floor Measurements (in.)

Number of Children

Plotting Points on a Coordinate Grid

1. Draw a dot on the number line for each number your teacher dictates. Also write the number under the dot.

```
<-+--+--+--+--+--+--+--+--+--+--+--+--+--+--+--+--+--+--+--+->
 -10                          0                            10
```

2. Draw a dot on the grid for each ordered pair. Write the letter for the ordered pair next to the dot.

Sample   A: (3,6)

B: (3,4)	C: (4,3)	D: (1,2)
E: (2,3)	F: (5,2)	G: (4,4)
H: (4,0)	I: (6,4)	J: (0,5)
K: (3,2)	L: (5,4)	M: (1,4)

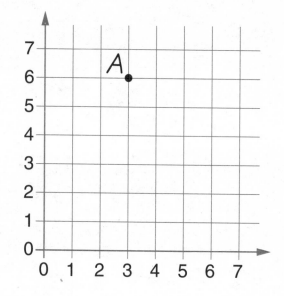

3. Do you know the answer to this riddle?

Which two letters contain nothing? To find out, draw the following line segments on the grid: $\overline{MD}$, $\overline{ME}$, $\overline{EB}$, $\overline{BK}$, $\overline{GI}$, and $\overline{LF}$.

_____

Draw the following line segments on the coordinate grid.

4. From (0,6) to (2,7); from (2,7) to (3,5); from (3,5) to (1,4); from (1,4) to (0,6)

What kind of quadrangle is this?

_____

5. From (7,0) to (7,4); from (7,4) to (5,3); from (5,3) to (5,1); from (5,1) to (7,0)

What kind of quadrangle is this?

_____

Using a Commuter Railroad Timetable

Solve the problems. Use your tool-kit clock if you need help.

Train Schedule	
South Chicago	11:46 A.M.
83rd Street	11:49
Cheltenham	11:51
South Shore	11:55
Bryn Mawr	11:57
59th Street	12:04 P.M.
Hyde Park	12:08
Kenwood	12:09
McCormick Place	12:14
18th Street	12:15
Van Buren Street	12:19
Randolph Street	12:22

1. About how many minutes is the trip from South Chicago to Randolph Street?

   _____

2. At what station will the train stop about 22 minutes after it leaves South Chicago?

   _____

3. At what station did the train stop about 25 minutes before it got to Randolph Street?

   _____

4. At what station does the train stop halfway through the trip—when about half of the total trip time has passed?

   _____

5. Marci got on the train at Cheltenham and got off at Kenwood. About how long was she on the train? _____

6. Make up two problems. Ask your partner to solve them.

   _____

   _____

   _____

   _____

   _____

Math Boxes 10.11

1. Find the distance between each pair of numbers.

4 and −19 _____

−23 and 46 _____

1,000 and −7,000 _____

2. Points scored by players in a basketball game:

15, 22, 11, 12, 5

The mean (average) number of points is _____.

77–79

3. What is the mode of the test scores for the class? _____%

Test Score	Number of Children
100%	///
95%	ЖЖ
90%	ЖЖ ///
85%	////

SRB
75 76

4. Complete.

Area of Base (square cm)	Height (cm)	Volume (cubic cm)
60	6	
45	4	
200	70	
80	80	

SRB
141

5. Read the scale and record the weight.

_____ lb

6. Complete.

1 pint = _____ fluid ounces

_____ pints = 48 fluid ounces

1 half-gallon = _____ quarts

_____ half-gallons = 6 quarts

1 liter = _____ milliliters

142 143

147 148

Math Boxes 10.12

1. When you flip a coin, it will land on

_____ or _____.

2. On which color is the spinner most likely to land? _____

Least likely to land? _____

3. True or false? It is unlikely that the spinner will land on blue.

_____

4. True or false? There is an equal chance of taking a B or an R block out of the bag.

_____

5. You and a friend are playing a game with a 6-sided die. You win if you roll an odd number. Your friend wins if you roll an even number. Do you think this game is fair? Circle one.

yes   no

6. You and a friend are playing a game with the spinner. You win if the spinner lands on purple. Your friend wins if the spinner lands on black. Do you think this game is fair?

yes

no

Can You Be Sure?

1. Make a list of things you are *sure* will happen.

_____

_____

_____

_____

_____

2. Make a list of things you are sure will *not* happen.

_____

_____

_____

_____

_____

3. Make a list of things you think *may* happen, but you are not sure.

_____

_____

_____

_____

_____

278 (two hundred seventy-eight)

Reading and Writing Numbers

Write the value of 7 for each column below.

L	K	J	I	H	G	F	E	D	.	C	B	A
hundred-millions	ten-millions	millions	hundred-thousands	ten-thousands	thousands	hundreds	tens	ones	.	tenths	hundredths	thousandths
7	7	7	7	7	7	7	7	7	.	7	7	7

Example Column K: ___70,000,000 or 70 million___

1. Column A: _____

2. Column G: _____

3. Column F: _____

4. Column I: _____

5. Column C: _____

6. Column B: _____

7. Column L: _____

Write the numbers that your teacher dictates.

8. _____

9. _____

10. _____

11. _____

12. _____

13. _____

Use with Lesson 11.1.

(two hundred seventy-nine) **279**

1. Plot and label each of the points listed below.

A: (1,4)

B: (2,2)

C: (3,1)

D: (4,3)

SRB 162 163

2. Cross out the names that do not belong.

$\frac{1}{5}$

$\frac{2}{10}$ $\frac{100}{500}$ $\frac{1}{8}$

$\frac{4}{5}$ $1\frac{1}{5}$ $\frac{5}{25}$

SRB 30

3. Weight in pounds of newborn babies: 11, 8, 8, 7, 6

The average (mean) weight is _____ pounds.

The weight that occurs most often (mode) is _____ pounds.

SRB 75–79

4. Insert <, >, or =.

5×9 _____ 7×7

8×9 _____ 6×8

4×8 _____ 3×9

7×8 _____ 9×9

SRB 13 46 47

5. Use the partial-products algorithm to solve.

$$\begin{array}{r} 83 \\ \times\,44 \\ \hline \end{array} \qquad \begin{array}{r} 72 \\ \times\,36 \\ \hline \end{array}$$

SRB 58 59

6. There are 347 candles. A box holds 50 candles. How many full boxes of candles is that?

_____ boxes

How many candles are left over?

_____ candles

SRB 68

Fill in the missing numbers.

1.

0   100

2.

26,000   27,000

Show the following on the metric ruler below.

3. Make a dot at 6.8 cm. Label it **A.**

4. Make a dot at 140 mm. Label it **B.**

5. Make a dot at 0.12 m. Label it **C.**

6. Make a dot at 9.5 cm. Label it **D.**

7. Make a dot at 12 mm. Label it **E.**

0 1 2 3 4 5 6 7 8 9 10 11 12 13 14 15

cm

Challenge

Fill in the missing numbers.

8.

−0.5   0   0.5

Math Boxes 11.2

1. Complete.

Area of Base (square feet)	Height (feet)	Volume (cubic feet)
40	90	
20	70	
800	9	
50	80	

2. Complete.

2 gallons = _____ quarts

_____ gallons = 16 quarts

2 pints = _____ cups

_____ pints = 20 cups

2 cups = _____ fl oz

_____ cups = 32 fl oz

3. Circle the event(s) that you are sure will happen.

It will be sunny tomorrow.

A tossed quarter will land on either heads or tails.

A rolled die will land on 6.

4. Name 3 objects that weigh about 1 gram.

_____

_____

_____

_____

5. Fill in the oval next to the best estimate.

5,634 − 2,987 = _____

○ about 2,000

○ about 2,300

○ about 2,600

○ about 3,000

6. Write six numbers that are factors of 32.

_____ _____ _____

_____ _____ _____

Use with Lesson 11.2.

Coin-Toss Experiment

Work with a partner. You need 10 coins.

1. Each of you takes turns tossing the 10 coins.

   For each toss you make,
   record the number of heads
   and the number of tails in the table.

   Toss the coins 5 times in all.

   Then find the total number of heads
   and tails.

My Toss Record

Toss (10 coins)	Heads	Tails
1		
2		
3		
4		
5		
Total		

My total: heads _____   tails _____

My partner's total: heads _____   tails _____

Our partnership total: heads _____   tails _____

2. Record the number of heads and the number of tails for the whole class.

   Number of heads: _____   Number of tails: _____

3. Suppose a jar contains 1,000 pennies.
   The jar is turned over. The pennies are
   dumped onto a table and spread out.
   Write your best guess for the number
   of heads and tails.

   Number of heads: _____   Number of tails: _____

Fractions

1. The shaded square is ONE. Write a name for the shaded part of each of the other shapes. The first one is done for you.

$\frac{1}{2}$ ___ ___ ___ ___ ___

2. The shaded rectangle is ONE. Write a name for the shaded part of each of the other shapes.

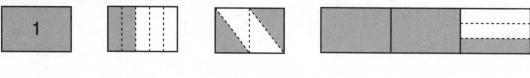

___   ___   ___   ___

Write <, >, or = to compare fractions.

3. $\frac{3}{5}$ ☐ $\frac{1}{2}$ 4. $\frac{3}{8}$ ☐ $\frac{3}{4}$ 5. $\frac{4}{6}$ ☐ $\frac{5}{9}$ 6. $\frac{3}{4}$ ☐ $\frac{9}{12}$ 7. $\frac{7}{10}$ ☐ $\frac{6}{12}$

8. Choose one comparison above and explain how you found your answer.

_____

_____

9. Write numbers in this name-collection box.

10. Make your own name-collection box. Write a fraction on the tag. Write numbers in the box.

Math Boxes 11.3

---

1. Plot and label each of the points listed below.

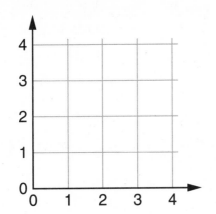

A: (1,2)

B: (3,3)

C: (4,1)

D: (2,4)

162 163

2. Fill in the unit box. Solve.

Unit

$5 \times 8 =$ _____

$4 \times 9 =$ _____

_____ $= 6 \times 7$

_____ $= 7 \times 9$

_____ $= 8 \times 8$

46 47

---

3. Goals scored by players during a soccer season: 14, 12, 8, 7, 8, 11

The average (mean) number of goals is _____.

The number of goals that occurs most often (mode) is _____.

75–79

4. Is a 6-sided die more likely to land on an odd number or an even number? Explain.

_____

_____

_____

_____

_____

84–86

---

5. Practice lattice multiplication.

$56 \times 78 =$ _____

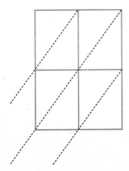
60–62

6. Fill in the missing numbers on the number line.

_____ _____ −4   2 _____

39 40

Spinners

Math Message

Color each circle so that it matches the description.

1.

$\frac{3}{4}$ red, $\frac{2}{8}$ blue

2.

$\frac{1}{2}$ red, $\frac{1}{3}$ yellow, $\frac{1}{6}$ blue

3.

$\frac{2}{5}$ red, $\frac{2}{5}$ blue, $\frac{1}{5}$ yellow

Spinner Experiments

Tape *Math Masters,* page 180, to your desk or table.
Make a spinner on the first circle.

4. Spin the paper clip 10 times. Tally the number of times the paper clip lands on the shaded part and on the white part.

Lands On	Tallies
shaded part	
white part	

5. Record results for the whole class.

Lands On	Totals
shaded part	
white part	

Make a spinner on the second circle.

6. Spin the paper clip 10 times. Tally the number of times the paper clip lands on the shaded part and on the white part.

Lands On	Tallies
shaded part	
white part	

7. Record results for the whole class.

Lands On	Totals
shaded part	
white part	

8. The paper clip has a better chance of landing on the _____ part of the spinner than on the _____ part.

Degrees in a Turn

Tell how many degrees are in each turn.

1. full turn _____

2. half-turn _____

3. quarter-turn _____

4. $\frac{3}{4}$ turn _____

5. $\frac{1}{3}$ turn _____

6. $\frac{2}{3}$ turn _____

7. $\frac{1}{6}$ turn _____

8. $\frac{2}{6}$ turn _____

9. $\frac{3}{6}$ turn _____

10. $\frac{5}{6}$ turn _____

Challenge

Tell how many degrees are in each turn.

11. $\frac{1}{2}$ of a half-turn _____

12. $\frac{1}{2}$ of a quarter-turn _____

13. $\frac{1}{3}$ of a half-turn _____

14. $\frac{1}{3}$ of a quarter-turn _____

Tell what fraction of a full turn each angle is.

15. 30° _____

16. 45° _____

1. Write 5 fractions that are greater than $\frac{9}{12}$.

_____ _____ _____ _____ _____

Write 5 fractions that are less than $\frac{9}{12}$.

_____ _____ _____ _____ _____

Write 3 other names for $\frac{9}{12}$.

_____ _____ _____

SRB 30

2. Complete.

2 quarts = _____ pints

_____ quarts = 30 pints

2 quarts = _____ fl oz

_____ quarts = 96 fl oz

2 gallons = _____ fl oz

SRB 142 143

3. Complete.

Area of Base (square inches)	Height (inches)	Volume (cubic inches)
100		900
50		3,500
20		1,800
70		4,200

SRB 139–141

4. Write the number that has

0 in the thousandths place

4 in the ones place

1 in the tenths place

8 in the hundredths place

___ . ___ ___ ___

SRB 35

5. Describe 2 events that have a "good chance" of happening.

_____

_____

_____

_____

_____

SRB 84–86

6. A van holds 8 people. 125 people are going to the concert. How many vans are needed?

_____ vans

Will all of the vans be full? _____

SRB 68

Math Boxes 11.5

---

1. Write the ordered pair for each letter on the grid.

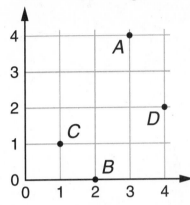

A: (____, ____)

B: (____, ____)

C: (____, ____)

D: (____, ____)

SRB 162 163

---

2. Color the circle so that it matches the description.

$\frac{1}{2}$ blue

$\frac{1}{3}$ green

$\frac{1}{6}$ yellow

Which color would you expect a spinner to land on most often?

_____

SRB 86

---

3. Number of books read by children during the summer: 9, 9, 5, 15, 3, 9, 6

The average (mean) number of books read is

_____.

The number of books read that occurs most often (mode) is

_____.

SRB 75–79

---

4. Insert <, >, or =.

4×6 _____ 2×9

7×7 _____ 5×9

6×7 _____ 9×4

8×6 _____ 9×7

SRB 46 13 47

---

5. Use the partial-products algorithm to solve.

$$\begin{array}{r} 77 \\ \times\ 24 \\ \hline \end{array} \qquad \begin{array}{r} 93 \\ \times\ 61 \\ \hline \end{array}$$

SRB 58 59

---

6. 6,570,321

The digit in the thousands place is _____.

The digit in the millions place is _____.

The digit in the hundred-thousands place is _____.

The digit in the tens place is _____.

SRB 18–21

Making Spinners

Math Message

1. Use exactly six different colors. Make a spinner so that the paper clip has the **same chance** of landing on any one of the six colors.

   (Hint: Into how many equal parts should the circle be divided?)

2. Use only blue and red. Make a spinner so that the paper clip is **twice as likely** to land on blue as it is to land on red.

Use with Lesson 11.5.

Making Spinners (cont.)

3. Use only blue, red, and green. Make a spinner so that the paper clip:

- has the **same chance** of landing on blue and on red

and

- is **less likely** to land on green than on blue.

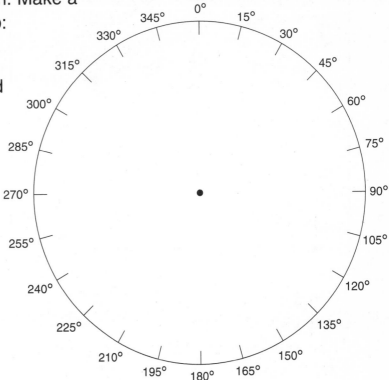

4. Use only blue, red, and yellow. Make a spinner so that the paper clip:

- is **more likely** to land on blue than on red

and

- is **less likely** to land on yellow than on blue.

Use with Lesson 11.5.   (two hundred ninety-one) **291**

Parentheses Puzzles

Circle the expressions that belong in each name-collection box.

1. | 7 |

$7 \times (8 - 7)$ $(5 + 5) - (3 - 1)$

$(3 \times 4) - 5$ $(3 \times 7) \div 7$

$(12 + 2) \div 2$ $(4 \times 7) \div (10 - 6)$

$(7 \times 1) \times 7$

2. | 25 |

$(4 + 1) \times (6 - 1)$ $100 \div (6 - 1)$

$(4 \times 5) + 5$ $(2 \times 10) \times 5$

$25 + (0 \times 10)$ $50 - (30 - 10)$

$(6 \times 5) - (1 \times 5)$

3. Fill in the tag.
Circle correct names.
Cross out incorrect names.
Add 2 names.

$5 + (10 \div 2)$ $9 + (10 \div 10)$

$(3 + 2) \times 2$ $(9 + 10) \div 10$

$(20 \div 4) + 5$ $4 + (2 \times 3)$

$2 + (4 \times 2)$

$(2 + 4) \times 2$

Add parentheses, ( ), to complete the number models.

4. $7 \times 8 - 8 = 48$

5. $7 \times 8 - 8 = 0$

6. $280 = 85 - 45 \times 22 - 15$

7. $80 \times 3 + 4 = 560$

Complete the number models.

8. _____ $= (24 \div 6) - 2$

9. _____ $= 24 \div (6 - 2)$

10. $(7 + 3) \times (9 + 6) =$ _____

11. $7 + (3 \times 9) + 6 =$ _____

Drawing Blocks

Color the blocks in the bags blue. Then fill in the blanks by answering this question: How many red blocks would you put into each bag?

1. If I wanted to have an equal chance of taking out red or blue, I would put in _____ red block(s).

2. If I wanted to be more likely to take out blue than red, I would put in _____ red block(s).

3. If I wanted to be sure of taking out a blue block, I would put in _____ red block(s).

4. If I wanted to take out a red block about 3 times as often as a blue one, I would put in _____ red block(s).

5. If I wanted to take out a red block about half as often as a blue one, I would put in _____ red block(s).

6. If I wanted to take out a red block about $\frac{1}{3}$ of the time, I would put in _____ red block(s).

Challenge

7. If I wanted to take out a red block about $\frac{2}{3}$ of the time, I would put in _____ red block(s).

The Best Pizza

Pizza Prices			
	10-inch serves 2–3	**12-inch** serves 3–4	**14-inch** serves 4–5
plain cheese	$8.35	$10.85	$12.40
each added topping	$1.25	$1.50	$1.75

Choices for added toppings: sausage, mushrooms, red or green peppers, onions, pepperoni, spinach, ground beef, extra cheese

1. How much does a 10-inch pizza with 1 added topping cost? $_____

2. How much does a 12-inch pizza with 2 added toppings cost? $_____

3. For the class pizza party, the class votes to order five 14-inch pizzas with one added topping on each pizza. How much will the pizzas cost? $_____

4. Which costs more? Circle your answer.

    3 of the 10-inch pizzas with 2 added toppings each

    2 of the 14-inch pizzas with 1 added topping each

5. Write and solve your own pizza number story.

    _____

    _____

    _____

    _____

Math Boxes 11.6

1. Find the volume of the rectangular prism.

Volume = _____ cubic units

2. Write six numbers that are factors of 100.

_____ _____ _____ _____

_____ _____ _____ _____

3. A large bag of candy costs $3.59. What is the cost of 6 bags?

Fill in the oval next to the best estimate.

◯ $15.00

◯ $18.00

◯ $21.00

◯ $24.00

4. Put the fractions in order from smallest to largest.

$\frac{1}{5}, \frac{1}{7}, \frac{3}{4}, \frac{5}{6}, \frac{99}{100}$

_____, _____, _____, _____, _____

5. Describe 2 events that are "not likely" to happen.

_____

_____

_____

_____

6. Draw a shape with an area of 10 square centimeters.

What is the perimeter of your shape? _____ centimeters

Random-Draw Problems

Each problem is about marbles in a jar. The marbles may be black, white, or striped. A marble is drawn at random from the jar (without looking into the jar). The kind of marble is tallied. Then the marble is returned to the jar.

- Decide, from the description of the random draws in each problem, how many marbles of each kind are in the jar.
- Shade the circles in the jar to match your decision.

1. From 100 random draws, you get:

   a black marble ● 62 times

   a white marble ○ 38 times

   10 marbles
   in a jar

2. From 50 random draws, you get:

   a black marble ● 30 times

   a white marble ○ 16 times

   a striped marble ① 4 times

   10 marbles
   in a jar

3. From 100 random draws, you get:

   a black marble ● 23 times

   a white marble ○ 53 times

   a striped marble ① 24 times

   8 marbles
   in a jar

Math Boxes 11.7

1. Write the ordered pair for each letter on the grid.

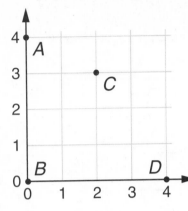

A: (____,____)

B: (____,____)

C: (____,____)

D: (____,____)

SRB
162 163

2. Write at least 5 names in the name-collection box.

$\frac{6}{10}$

SRB
30

3. Laps completed during practice by members of the swim team:
10, 15, 20, 15, 15

The average (mean) number of laps completed is ____.

The number of laps that occurs most often (mode) is ____.

SRB
75–79

4. Design a spinner that has an equal chance of landing on red as it does of landing on green.

SRB
86

5. Practice lattice multiplication.

$73 \times 39 =$ _____

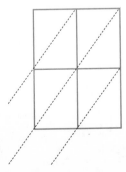

SRB
60–62

6. If I wanted to have an equal chance of taking out a circle or a square, I would put in

____ circle(s).

Math Boxes 11.8

1. Find the volume of the rectangular prism.

Volume = _____ cubic units

2. Describe 2 events that are "impossible."

_____

_____

_____

_____

_____

3. 10 marbles in a jar.
100 random draws.

You get:
a black marble ● 32 times
a white marble ○ 68 times

How many marbles of each kind do you think are in the jar?

_____ black marbles

_____ white marbles

4. Complete.

2 pints = _____ fl oz

_____ pints = 96 fl oz

2 half-gallons = _____ quarts

_____ half-gallons = 10 quarts

5 liters = _____ milliliters

5. If I wanted to take out a square about 4 times as often as a circle,

I would put in _____ square(s).

6. 9,457,023

The digit in the ten-thousands place is _____.

The digit in the millions place is _____.

The digit in the hundreds place is _____.

The digit in the ones place is _____.

Estimate—Then Calculate

Solve only the problems whose sum or difference is greater than 500.

1.
$$825 - 347$$

2.
$$984 - 392$$

3.
$$658 - 179$$

4.
$$324 + 161$$

5.
$$728 - 232$$

6.
$$227 + 285$$

7.
$$174 + 338$$

8.
$$881 - 293$$

9.
$$1{,}294 - 776$$

1. A baker packs 835 doughnuts into boxes that hold a dozen doughnuts each. How many full boxes does he pack?

_____ boxes

How many doughnuts are left over?

_____ doughnuts

2. Design a spinner that is twice as likely to land on blue as it is to land on yellow.

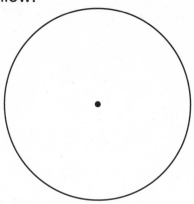

3. Draw a shape with a perimeter of 20 centimeters.

What is the area of your shape?

_____ square centimeters

4. If I wanted to take out a circle about $\frac{1}{3}$ of the time, I would put in _____ circle(s).

5. Use the partial-products algorithm to solve.

```
  82        94
× 35      × 76
```

6. 10 marbles in a jar.
100 random draws.

You get:
a black marble ● 23 times
a white marble ○ 77 times

How many marbles of each kind do you think are in the jar?

_____ black marbles

_____ white marbles

Math Boxes 11.10

1. Plot and label each of the points listed below.

A: (0,3)

B: (3,0)

C: (2,4)

D: (4,2)

SRB
162 163

2. Write a fraction in the tag. Fill the name-collection box with equivalent fractions.

SRB
30

3. Find the volume of the rectangular prism.

Volume = _____ cubic units

SRB
139–141

4. Put these numbers in order from smallest to largest.

0.45, −6, −0.3, 4, −4.5

_____ , _____ , _____ ,

_____ , _____

SRB
36

5. Write the number that has

5 in the thousandths place

6 in the ones place

3 in the tenths place

9 in the hundredths place

___ . ___ ___ ___

SRB
35

6. Solve.

```
  5,673
+   489
```

```
  4,008
− 3,959
```

SRB
51–57

Special Pages

The following pages will be used throughout the remainder of the school year.

	Pages
National High/Low Temperature Project	303
Temperature Ranges	304 and 305
Length of Day	306 and 307
Sunrise and Sunset Record	308

For the National High/Low Temperature Project on journal page 303, you will continue to record the following data: the U.S. city with the highest temperature and the U.S. city with the lowest temperature for the same date. You will do this every week or whenever your teacher tells you. This is the same thing that you did on journal page 160 in your *Math Journal 1.*

The data that you recorded on journal pages 160 and 303 will be used in Unit 7 on journal pages 304 and 305 to make a Temperature Ranges graph. Your teacher will teach you how to do this.

On journal page 306, you will have to copy your graph from page 158 in your *Math Journal 1,* and then continue to add to the graph on pages 306 and 307.

On journal page 308, you will continue to collect data as you did on page 158 in your *Math Journal 1.* You will continue to record the date, and the sunrise and sunset times for that date.

During Unit 11, you will use the information that you have collected on these pages and discuss the graphs that you have made.

National High/Low Temperatures Project

Date	Highest Temperature		Lowest Temperature		Difference in Temperature
	Place	Temperature	Place	Temperature	
		°F		°F	°F
		°F		°F	°F
		°F		°F	°F
		°F		°F	°F
		°F		°F	°F
		°F		°F	°F
		°F		°F	°F
		°F		°F	°F
		°F		°F	°F
		°F		°F	°F
		°F		°F	°F
		°F		°F	°F
		°F		°F	°F
		°F		°F	°F
		°F		°F	°F
		°F		°F	°F
		°F		°F	°F
		°F		°F	°F
		°F		°F	°F
		°F		°F	°F
		°F		°F	°F

Use with Lesson 7.8.

Temperature Ranges

Use with Lesson 7.8.

Temperature Ranges (cont.)

Date

Length of Day

16 hr 0 min

30 min

15 hr 0 min

30 min

14 hr 0 min

30 min

13 hr 0 min

30 min

12 hr 0 min

30 min

11 hr 0 min

30 min

10 hr 0 min

30 min

9 hr 0 min

30 min

8 hr 0 min

Date

306 (three hundred six)

Use with Lesson 7.1.

Date _____   Time _____

16 hr 0 min

30 min

15 hr 0 min

30 min

14 hr 0 min

30 min

13 hr 0 min

30 min

12 hr 0 min

30 min

11 hr 0 min

30 min

10 hr 0 min

30 min

9 hr 0 min

30 min

8 hr 0 min

Date

Sunrise and Sunset Record

Date	Time of Sunrise	Time of Sunset	Length of Day
			hr min
			hr min
			hr min
			hr min
			hr min
			hr min
			hr min
			hr min
			hr min
			hr min
			hr min
			hr min
			hr min
			hr min
			hr min
			hr min
			hr min
			hr min
			hr min
			hr min

Use with Lesson 7.8.

Date _____ Time _____

Notes

Notes

Notes

Date _____ Time _____

Notes

_____

_____

_____

_____

_____

_____

_____

_____

_____

_____

_____

_____

_____

_____

Date _____ Time _____

×, ÷ Fact Triangles 3

Activity Sheet 5

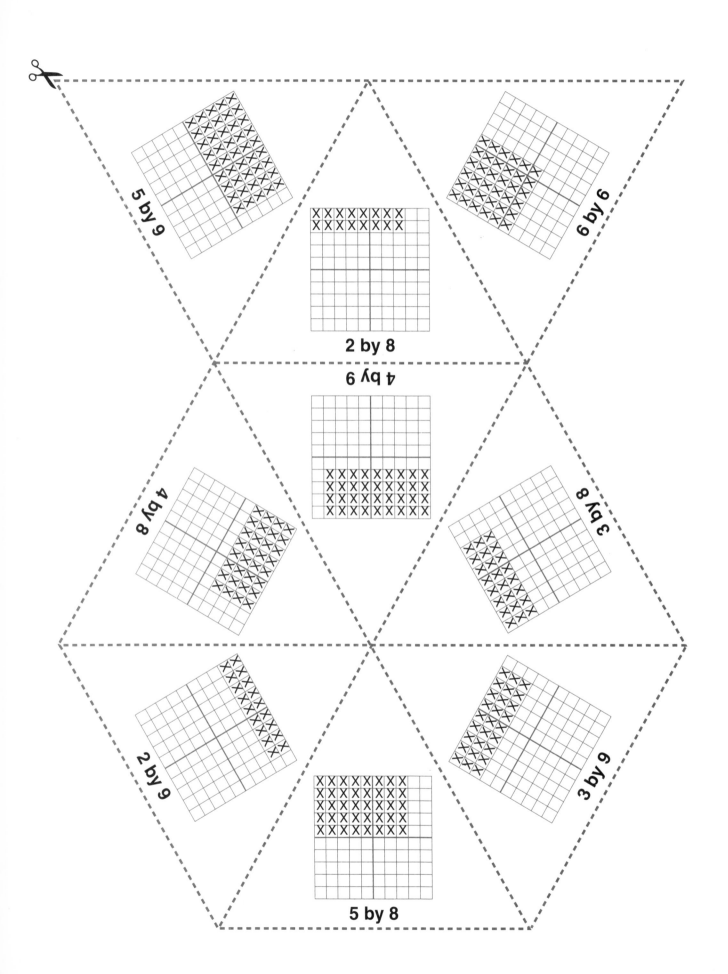

×, ÷ Fact Triangles 4

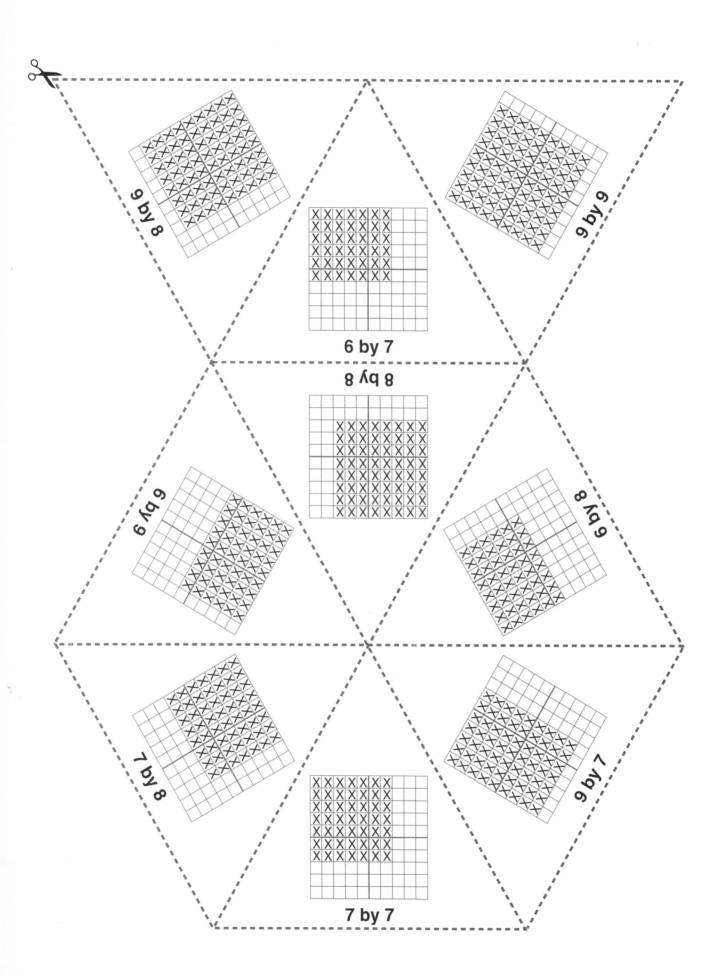

Fraction Cards

$\frac{1}{2}$

$\frac{3}{6}$

$\frac{1}{3}$

$\frac{2}{2}$

$\frac{2}{6}$

$\frac{1}{4}$

$\frac{2}{3}$

$\frac{3}{4}$

$\frac{2}{4}$

$\frac{6}{8}$

$\frac{0}{2}$

$\frac{4}{6}$

$\frac{4}{8}$

$\frac{0}{4}$

$\frac{2}{8}$

$\frac{4}{4}$

$$\frac{2}{2} \qquad \frac{1}{3} \qquad \frac{3}{6} \qquad \frac{1}{2}$$

$$\frac{3}{4} \qquad \frac{2}{3} \qquad \frac{1}{4} \qquad \frac{2}{6}$$

$$\frac{4}{6} \qquad \frac{0}{2} \qquad \frac{6}{8} \qquad \frac{2}{4}$$

$$\frac{4}{4} \qquad \frac{2}{8} \qquad \frac{0}{4} \qquad \frac{4}{8}$$

Back of Activity Sheet 7

Fraction Cards

Use with Lesson 8.4.

Activity Sheet 8

$$\frac{6}{12}$$ $$\frac{3}{9}$$ $$\frac{8}{12}$$ $$\frac{5}{10}$$

$$\frac{2}{12}$$ $$\frac{5}{6}$$ $$\frac{9}{12}$$ $$\frac{1}{6}$$

$$\frac{2}{10}$$ $$\frac{3}{12}$$ $$\frac{6}{9}$$ $$\frac{1}{5}$$

$$\frac{8}{10}$$ $$\frac{10}{12}$$ $$\frac{4}{5}$$ $$\frac{4}{12}$$